MRS FRAM

Mrs Frampton

PAM GEMS

BLOOMSBURY

First published 1989
This paperback edition published 1990
Copyright © 1989 by Pam Gems

Bloomsbury Publishing Ltd, 2 Soho Square; London W1V 5DE

British Library Cataloguing in Publication Data
Gems, Pam
  Mrs. Frampton.
  I. Title
  823.'914 [F]
  ISBN 0-7475-0592-6

Typeset by Columns of Reading
Printed in Great Britain by Richard Clay Ltd, Bungay, Suffolk

Numero Uno, Pueblo La Jolla, near Malaga, might be a long way from Bradford to May Frampton, but by heck, it was champion.

The Framptons were forced to retire here because of Vic's bronchitis, or else the old sod would never have budged. It was true those daft Frenchwomen out by the pool always managed to raise May's blood pressure, the way they whinnied on about sex, clothes and money. But May had her lovely garden and room for her son and daughter to stay – if they could ever get away.

It was a laugh to begin to feel part of the place: to see how the Spanish men outwitted the tourists and how the women held their heads high as they grew older – not the 'excuse-me-for-living' apology of the British matron. Vic naturally complained about the cost of her Spanish lessons, but what was the point if you didn't have a go?

That pluck is precisely what attracted the diminutive widow from Hong Kong, the elusive May Liu, to May Frampton. No one at the Country Club could understand how the forthright northerner 'pudding' had been singled out. 'Big May' and 'Little May', they called the extraordinary-looking duo who couldn't have cared less what anyone said. The friends shared a love of beautiful things – of flowers and of paintings – and a goodness of heart that is worth knowing about.

You can't help but spot the comic side of life in the company of Mrs Frampton, but she keeps her eye out for the more dangerous pitfalls of human nature. Pride has its place but also its limits. Cooked-up chic and pretension can go hang. Loyalty and grit, a keen sense of adventure and a keener sense of the absurd are what lie at the core of this supremely winning novel and its unforgettable heroine.

Chapter 1

IT WAS AMAZING how many sounds you could hear if you sat with your eyes closed. Most insistent was the puck-puck sound of the traps at the side of the swimming pool, becoming a puck-puck-puck-puck-puck clatter of sound as somebody dived in. You'd think they could find a better idea than that noise. What else? The clatter of cutlery as one of the waiters put down an order at a nearby table. An aeroplane, a little one, droning high up in the sky. The hum of a car, then another, and another. And dying away again. A dog yelping, tied up somewhere in a yard no doubt – the way they treated their dogs! Now a speedboat, whoosh, quite close, making a devil of a row, almost drowning the quack of voices on the terrace.

They were still on about it. Kirsta, the Danish woman with the embroidery, who usually had more sense, was asking round the table.

'Eliette?'

Oh, not her! Now it would get stupid. But the French-woman, after a pause and a dismissive sigh, said no, she didn't think so.

'What about you, May?'

Mrs Frampton opened her eyes and sat up, blinking against the sun, as Lyn, the young English girl with the mother, leaned forward.

'You know, Mrs Frampton . . . the little Spanish chap who lives over the café!'

'The aparrtment weeth the red flowers . . . '

'Red, red, red!'

That was the third Frenchwoman, the one who did nothing but shriek. All three Frenchies began to snigger inexplicably.

'What, you mean his begonias?'

The snickers became howls of laughter.

1

Mrs Frampton, grinding her teeth, thought That's right, whinny away, you fools!

What were they on about? What was wrong with the man's flowers? They were a lovely splodge of colour. The contrast between the scarlet blooms and his white window boxes was really crisp. Eliette, the skinny Frenchwoman, leaned back in her chair, showing the tops of her bridges in a lid-drooping smile.

'You know he ees a widower now?'

'I had heard,' said Mrs Frampton.

Why in the world had she bothered to sit down? It was always the same with the Frogs. One way or another they managed to raise your blood pressure . . . if it wasn't your hair it was your clothes; if it wasn't your clothes it was your sex life. Why couldn't they leave it alone? Where was her handbag? She shouldn't sit here by the smaller pool. This was the Frenchwomen's territory and they never let you forget it.

From the moment they were driven through the gates of the small and secluded Pueblo La Jolla Mrs Frampton had thought Yes! She had asked for the car to be stopped so they could walk through the gardens to the estate office. The gardens! White lilies and blue agapanthus bordering a long, narrow pool with discreet fountains and, beyond feathery pepper trees, flower-beds heavy with pale poppies and amaryllis – and everything flowering at once!

'Oh Vic!' she had whispered.

But, as usual, his arms full of rival brochures, he had been too busy to see anything.

'Don't start going stupid.'

In the office they were shown a model of the pueblo. Thankfully, it was, just, complete. They would not be living in an on-going building site. To the east a cluster of older houses was almost hidden in pines, to the west there was a sand-pit and a small stream which bordered a huge white house, the property, said the salesman, of a wealthy Arab. The trouble was there weren't many apartments left for sale. One was over the pueblo café and restaurant, so that was out, and the other three were at the back with only squinty views of the sea. And they were small.

'We do avunass,' said the salesman gently.

'Avunass?'

'Unass,' he said firmly, and pointed to the western end of the model.

'Oh . . . a house!'

'We don't want a house.'

'Hang on a minute, Vic.'

That had got her a dirty look but she had persisted.

'It's not a big house.'

'It's got three bedrooms!'

'They're only small, and one leads off an archway, it's not properly separate, it's two, really.'

The salesman took down a key.

'We might as well. Now we're here. As you say, it's useful for comparison.'

The house at the western end of the development, low and discreet like the others, stood almost alone, linked only to its neighbour by a bathroom over a Moorish arch which shaded the little path to the beach.

'What do we want with a house with three bedrooms?'

'Guests! Look at this, Vic.'

Enchanted, she wandered from the main room with its traditional fireplace to the sunbaked patio and the little garden. Over the patio a vine grew already – they certainly knew how to get round you!

'And look, Vic . . . a wall fountain!'

'How much?'

She could see by his face that it wasn't going to be any good. The price was almost double what they had in mind. Damn. This was the place she wanted. Nothing else had come anywhere near it. She talked fast, about the nearness to the shops, the beach, the exclusiveness of the development, its certain increase in value.

'We've come down here to buy an apartment. I keep telling you, we don't want a house.'

In the end there had been a dreadful silence. The salesman had looked at his feet. Mrs Frampton had refused to move.

And then the miracle had happened. Miserable, she had walked into the garden again and onto the patch of unmade ground beyond the gate.

'What's this?'

The salesman had shrugged. It was nothing. Anything they wished. Trees would be planted, it would be landscaped for them.

'I'd like that as a garden,' Mrs Frampton heard herself saying. 'Will you throw it in for the same price?'

They were both utterly amazed when this was conceded on the spot with an amiable wave of the hand. HE'd cleared his throat and then said nothing. Over the celebratory sherry in the *oficina* she had felt a rare surge of exultation. She'd won. For once in her life, she'd got her own way. HE had been impressed by the two pools, though neither of them owned a costume or intended to exhibit themselves. Women far bigger than she oiled themselves daily and she admired their pluck and their determination to enjoy what they had paid for. But it wasn't for her. Bodies were to do with love or babies. Or illness. The sight of so many collapsed, obese shapes, perhaps because she had been a nurse, depressed her. Still, HE was proud of the generous lay-out and garage space, the many facilities and the competitive running charges.

'They've undersold, no doubt about it!'

It was true. They'd got a bargain.

The glory of the pueblo was the big pool, mosaic-tiled in dark blue with dolphins, leading, via the stepped gardens, to a smaller pool by the café and bar. The big pool was used by the few young people in the pueblo and by the staff and their friends. It drove him mad that the Spaniards came in droves at the weekend, filling the café tables and making use of the amenities.

'They've no right to be here; who's paying . . . We are!'

But every time he complained to Emilio, the porter, all he got was a sympathetic nod. The chap was supposed to be there to look after the owners, not let in all his relations from the villages up in the hills. His moaning would spread to the Spanish character, the Spanish government, even to the weather.

'Now you can't complain about the weather, Vic.'

That usually shut him up. His sudden bout of bronchitis had gone into pneumonia. A specialist had been called. For twenty years she had tried to persuade him abroad without success. Books from the library were the nearest she'd ever got to the Grand Canal. It had taken one short illness. The business was sold within eight months and here they were. Where she had always wanted to be. Out of the drizzle and in the south of somewhere. There it was, outside her window. The cradle of civilisation. The Mediterranean.

I shan't need to read so much, now. I'm here . . .

She had come with an open mind and been happy from the first day in the *pensión*, watching a little man sing with strange hoarse trills as he tiled a roof. And the food! The markets! Fish still quivering, vegetables smelling of earth, loquats, custard apples, tiny pink bananas from the Canaries.

I shall never stop eating!

But her stomach had gone down. The food was light and they walked every day, for his lungs. The more she settled, shopping, doing her Spanish, the more morose HE became. Nothing was right . . . but then, had it ever been? Only yesterday she had enthused over the generosity of the man in the *drogería* who had let her off forty *pesetas* to save her changing a big note, only to have him snarl at her.

'They want the change for their bloody payphones.'

It was true, you had to wait ages for your own line.

'All right, then, what about the man in the paper shop? He gave me a box of liquorice allsorts. For nothing.'

'You'll learn.'

'Learn what?'

'Once they've got your custom, the greasy bastards – '

'Now that's enough, Vic.'

She had never liked swearing.

'Join the Common Market? They haven't even got a proper banking system!'

There had been a dreadful three months while they were still in the *pensión*. A two thousand pound float, telexed from home to their new bank in San Pedro, had gone astray. Money sent via Madrid, they were informed by neighbours, had a habit of going walkabout. She thought he would go into apoplexy one morning in the bank manager's office. Mrs Frampton had felt sorry for the young chap, speaking his funny English without consonants.

'Ih wiy be yeer soo.'

But it wasn't, and when eventually, after more money had been sent to get them out of a hole, it had turned up in a small branch in Valencia, HE'd been in a black rage for a week because of the lost interest. But at last they were in. Settled. With new beds, new easy chairs, patio furniture, the lot. In a pueblo. In Spain. In the sun.

The older women sat by the smaller pool. During the day there would be one, sometimes several groups at the pierced, plastic tables under the white umbrellas. The Dutchwoman with the big legs spent most of the day there with Phyllis, who'd left her husband, and there was Kirsta, the Danish lady, Mrs Coombs and deaf Mrs Miller, Lyn and her mother and the French, who had the best houses in the pueblo apart from her own.

Mrs Frampton lay back with her eyes closed. It was always the same with the French. Sex, food and money. Nothing they ever talked about had anything to do with her. Who cared about fifteen ways of making mayonnaise? Anyway, it was bad for you. Why couldn't they leave it alone? Eliette, the tall one, was on again and now they all joined in about the little Spanish chap . . . his height, his small feet, his dead wife.

Why must they?

Stung by a comment from the hennaed one, she lifted herself up, hearing her voice more North Country than ever, despite herself.

'Heck, do you talk like that about me when I'm not here?'

'Spice of life, love.'

That was Lyn of the daft laugh.

'I don't see Señor García's love life has got anything to do with anybody.' *And* she'd pronounced García wrong.

'Not at all . . . it is fascinating!'

This was Henriette, the third Frenchwoman . . . well, she'd got fascinating wrong.

Silly fools.

6

Mrs Frampton, hot and cross, got up and walked off, aware of a slight hush and then a prattle of sound.

'Go on, sticks and stones.'

Without thinking, and for the first time, she went into the bar on her own. And ordered a lemonade. Sitting on a banquette by the strelitzias, she thought Cows. And fumed. But then the young waiter put down the little pitcher of fresh lemon juice, the jug of water, the ice, the sugar in the lidded tin.

'Thank you.'

'*De nada*,' he said softly, and smiled, making her feel better. Let them laugh. He was a nice little man, the Spaniard. He'd carried her string bag for her one day. And now he'd lost his wife. Poor chap. He looked thoroughly miserable.

'Now we've got rid of the English pudding,' said the tallest Frenchwoman in her own language, 'who is going to cherish the little Spanish?'

'Without doubt, little . . . '

'But not, I think, incapable.'

There was a thoughtful silence.

'It would be an act of politeness . . . '

'Perhaps, since I have been longest in the pueblo . . . '

'Oh but no!'

'You don't think . . . '

'Zut!'

'Very well, whoever wins at the tables tonight . . . agreed?'

'Yes, yes, yes!'

They laughed and Lyn, who had not understood a word, laughed too. Two storeys up, over the café, Señor Luis Antonio García, missing his wife, struggled to make his *tortilla* as Mrs Frampton, savagely shredding carrots in her kitchen, mixed her own blood with the coral slivers.

'We're not having salad again, are we?' asked her husband, coming in from a morning's golf, his appetite sharpened.

'It's good for you.'

'No thanks.'

They ate their cold beef and potatoes in silence.

'Trifle?'

She was usually on a winner there.

'What's happened to the cherries?'

'I ran out.'

Now he would sulk all afternoon. And the cut on her finger meant that she couldn't do her sewing. She said, 'Fancy a drive?' but got only a grunt in reply.

'All very well for you, you've been out all morning. We could look at Istan.'

'What for?'

'They say it's a lovely little village. Unspoiled.'

'Mucky, you mean.'

'All right, I'll go on my own!'

In the kitchen she suddenly thought of the little Señor García and his gentle, brown eyes and the pleasant lines on his face.

I suppose one of the Frenchies will get him.

She sighed. Pity.

Chapter 2

M RS FRAMPTON WAS sipping an apricot juice at her favourite harbour café. She had enjoyed her bath that morning. The airlock in the pipes seemed to have righted itself and there had been a decent flow of water. HE'd had his usual shower and, as usual, had reminded Mrs Frampton of the extra water needed for a bath. As usual, she had said nothing beyond calling out brightly, 'Just going down the road for a stroll,' as he rattled his *Daily Telegraph*.

It was hot. Mrs Frampton was wearing her cloth hat and mirror sunglasses. They looked silly but they kept out the glare; besides, you could watch people.

The Sunday morning market was already bubbling. More tourists this week, and more foreign flags on the boats in the marina. She noticed an unaccustomed languor among the local families parading with their children. It had been the week of the horse fair and the men, in particular, walked with an apologetic air. Two young Germans paused to buy plastic sandals. Nice young couple, pity about his neck. Filmy Indian scarves lifted in the breeze on the stall opposite, and the man on the bricabrac kicked a yellow ball and played with his baby son.

To the right, the tall, heavy man with the gold tooth on the art stall stood laughing with his brother. Brother, not so heavy, wore a blue safari suit and Italian shoes.

Still looks like a gyppo, thought Mrs Frampton as Gold Tooth broke away to accost approaching customers.

'How much?'

It was an Englishman, tall and thin with pale blue eyes and a reddening nose. His wife, stouter, was peering at an oil-painting of some chickens. There were two others and she moved her face along and back, and along again. Mrs Frampton knew the paintings well. They had been on the stall for several weeks.

'For thees one,' said Gold Tooth, flipping the painting down and nearly giving the woman a nose-job, 'for thees one . . . ' He screwed up his face in a moment of pain, and then relented with a smile of rueful submission which made him resemble Stalin.

'Thirty thousan' pesetas.'

The Englishman made a quick calculation and his wife assumed a bad smell expression to denote lack of interest.

'A hundred and forty pounds!' Mrs Frampton was tempted to call. But didn't.

'Let's see . . . good Lord, no, must be wrong. A hundred and forty pounds? Man's mad.'

The wife had a loud English voice of a certain class, posh and unpleasant. Mrs Frampton froze in automatic hate. See if they could pay that! Still, it was a bit stiff.

The English couple attempted to move on.

'These mouse-droppings want the chicken,' called Gold Tooth to his brother who was chatting intimately to the scarf girl.

'Sell them all three,' barked Brother without looking round.

'Agreed!'

And Gold Tooth took off after the English.

Mrs Frampton waved her hand for another apricot juice and then decided, for it would probably give her the runs, on a *café con leche* instead. The couple, moving on from the stall with the brick-hard homemade bread, were cut off by Gold Tooth at the hippie stall. They stood, blocking all view of the hippies' modest offerings, but this did not matter since the hippies were lowest in the pecking order, being incapable of beating anyone up. Their manner was ingratiating and Mrs Frampton, now that her Spanish was coming on a treat, knew just what the Spanish thought of that. Above the bubble of the fountain and the buzz of the market she caught snatches of interchange.

' . . . they're only Sunday paintings . . . '

'Interesting brushwork, though.'

And, sure enough, they returned, with Gold Tooth in dominating attachment. She watched, safe behind her sunglasses as the pictures were examined afresh.

'No provenance, of course.'

'Still . . . charming.'

Gold Tooth banged the painting hard to prove that it was on wood.

'The painter rahlly knows his chickens, ha ha.'

'Yers, terrific affection, almost a sort of wit.'

Gold Tooth wetted a finger and rubbed at the picture as all the dealers did when making a sale, to prove that under the grime was a possible masterpiece.

'*Antiguo!*'

'Nonsense, man, they're new. Modern!' He shouted slightly, as he was talking to a foreigner.

'*Nuevo!*' said the wife, with a roguish tilt of the head towards Gold Tooth.

'*Nuevo? No!*' was the shocked reply. '*No nuevo . . . nuevo, no!*'

It was getting exciting. A four hundred pound sale! Were they really valuable? Was the Englishman on to something? Who was having who on? Gold Tooth was pressing for another offer. The English moved apart and conferred. And returned.

'Eighteen thousand for the three.'

But that was only forty pounds apiece! Gold Tooth staggered predictably and scrawled an immediate counter offer.

'Fortitude, Carlos,' called Brother, who had been joined by the scarf girl's mother and family. 'Go for the shoulder blades!'

'Testicles!' shouted Gold Tooth hoarsely and, to the English, 'Thirty-two thousan' pesetas. Last price.'

The English went in conference again. And returned with a verbal offer of nineteen thousand. And strolled off purposefully at Tooth's attempt at a counter. Mrs Frampton leaned forward to witness the discomfiture of the brothers.

'How much?'

'They will go to twenty.'

Brother did a stylish and laconic flamenco turn. But the English had gone – they hadn't bought! Mrs Frampton drank down her coffee and picked up her two slips. Really, the Spanish did live in a fantasy world. She looked for the waiter and then sank back. No hurry. She could see the English in the distance, bending over a large bronze deer.

'Ach!' honked Gold Tooth in alarm.

But the English abandoned the deer and paused, dithering. And then turned back.

'She's coming!' shrieked the scarf girl, her bird cry quelled by a lurching nudge from Brother. The Englishwoman paused and bought one of the indigestible loaves. She began to move away and Gold Tooth, who had seated himself magisterially in his battered director's chair, got up and followed, cutting off her retreat by the stall with the hideously painted stones.

'How much? Your very best price. Sir . . . madam . . . as my friend, your best price, please.'

The Englishwoman wavered. She approached and bent towards the pictures.

'What do they want with chickens, they can't eat them!' shrieked the scarf girl, overcome by her own wit.

'Shut up,' suggested Brother.

'Please . . . best price . . . best price!'

'Tempting,' said the Englishman, scratching his behind and then disguising the gesture.

'They'd make a marvellous talking point,' said the wife. 'What do you think?'

This time, their private conversation was prolonged. Too prolonged. Even Mrs Frampton could see that their conflab by the pavement palm was a face-save. They'd had it. They returned for an attempt at surrender with honour. Gold Tooth stuck out for thirty, the English for nineteen. Tooth, displaying clinical depression, murmured twenty-five thousand with a limp, conceding wave. Yes . . . no? But Mrs English, flushed, demanded a piece of paper. Eighteen thousand or nothing.

But that was the original offer, thought Mrs Frampton, waving away the waiter. You'll need to do better than that.

The crowd was now augmented by the false Roman glass man and a cross-eyed girl in a bikini. A ginger dog came and sat down in the middle like an arbiter.

The Englishman wavered.

'Twenty thousand? Certainly not more.'

'They *are* lovely. Shall we be devils?'

'I'll have to go to the car for some cash.'

This caused a flurry of anxiety. Tooth pressed the paintings urgently into the Englishwoman's arms. He said in Spanish, 'Leave me a deposit, stable-scrapings. Look, see how I trust them, I am a romantic fool, judge me if you will!'

The English couple left with placating gestures and Gold Tooth placed the pictures under the palm tree, indicating to the woman that she must on no account fear that he might be tempted in their absence by a more lustrous offer.

Silence reigned.

No one looked at the brothers. Mrs Frampton sensed a growing sympathy towards them. Would the tourists return? The cross-eyed girl wandered away. Brother whistled a love song. Mrs Frampton beckoned the waiter and searched for change. The dog panted.

It was Mrs Frampton who weakened. She couldn't help it. Sheltered by the waiter she turned and half rose. And was thus the first to see the English on their measured return down the slope. Unable to resist, she waved and nodded at Tooth who looked back in benign indifference. But he knew. By the time the English arrived, his face was a rictus of smiling happiness. Brother, grinning broadly, put an arm about the scarf girl, fatally compromising himself in front of her family. The money was counted into Tooth's massive palm, the pictures were formally spat upon and reverently wiped before the final and formal handover.

'All right, do you think?'

'Charming . . . you *are* clever!'

Brother gazed in awe as the English strode away.

'Who would need not one but *three*, *three* pictures of hens . . . of hens!'

By his side the scarf girl's mother smiled deeply and embraced him with a menacingly seraphic smile.

'*Vino*!' honked Gold Tooth to universal shouts of joy. And Mrs Frampton almost forgot herself and followed as the crowd moved to the bar at the back of the pavement. She smiled to herself and rose. Time to get back. She hadn't a notion of what to provide for lunch. Every day, seven days a week, breakfast, lunch, tea and supper, in the end you felt like serving stewed slipper or a fricassee of spit. A spaghetti would be the easiest, with a mushroom sauce. If HE wanted meat, and he would, she could open a tin of ham. She picked up her cloth bag from the chair. As she did so something caught the edge of her eye. It was the little fat man who assisted Gold Tooth. He was taking something from the back of an ancient van. It was a picture. Of chickens. He placed it reverently on the stall and turned in self-important charge to fetch one, no, two, no, three more pictures of chickens. They had stacks of them!

Inside the bar the celebration had already begun. A burst of music and laughter followed Mrs Frampton up the rise. At the top, as she paused, panting for breath, a brown Volvo inched forward, waiting to edge out into the Sunday traffic. Inside, the two English gazed snootily forward in their dark glasses, craning slightly like a couple of . . . yes, like a couple of hens. You could see their chicken pictures, lovingly laid on the back seat. Mrs Frampton felt a sudden glorious surge of energy. Bugger cooking, she would make him take her out to lunch! They would come back here to the port for some seafood or drive up to the Greek restaurant beyond King Fahd's palace and the beautiful gardens belonging to the rich Chinawoman. How could you stick indoors on such a marvellous, such a hilarious day? And what did it matter if the English couple had paid too much? They were happy, Gold Tooth was happy. The thing was to do what you wanted, but with assurance. She went in the front way, straight through the sitting-room to the terrace, where HE was still sitting with his paper, half asleep.

'We're eating out. Come on, chop-chop. You can take me out to lunch.'

'What?'

But she already had his straw hat in her hand.

'I'll drive.'

To her surprise, he followed her along the path to the garages without a word.

Chapter 3

M RS FRAMPTON WAS in a foul humour. Although it was April,
they had had rain for three weeks. Every day, picking
up her English paper from Emilio, the porter, she read the
weather reports from home. Where there was a mini heatwave.

Over the breakfast pots she had tried to be philosophic.

I don't really mind the rain. It's good for the garden. If all
the reservoirs are filled up perhaps we shan't have the water
turned off this summer.

But enough was enough. Every blessed day, it began to get
you down. First the mist rolled over the mountain and then the
rain bucketed down, knocking over the irises and turning the
roses into sopping heaps of wet washing. The atmosphere
seemed more water than air and Mrs Frampton began to get
her sinuses again. Her face felt as it had in Bradford, boarded
up.

Oh, blast the weather.

The Spanish didn't seem to mind. When you grumbled they
seemed surprised. At first she had written this off as national
pride or commercial anxiety.

I expect they're worried about the holiday season.

But it was neither. People rarely carried umbrellas. They
walked, hatless and coatless in the rain, women with neat hair,
men in business suits, children splashing happily in the gutters,
swinging their satchels.

'The trouble with the Spanish is they're all touched by sun,'
HE grumbled, as always, out of synchronisation.

'There hasn't *been* any sun!'

But their reactions *were* different. She was reminded of the
Arabs in Tangier. As soon as you docked they were round the
car, all swearing they were official, trying to wrest your papers
away. And offering themselves as guides at the same time,

saying they knew the best restaurants, the best shops. Left in the car, alarmed and then sleepy, she had noticed how thin the men were. They all had something wrong with them, crossed eyes, broken teeth, twisted limbs.

Poor things. They're a mothy lot. Whoever's in charge here is no good.

After a longish wait she got out of the car.

'Vic! You have to give them some money. Him over there and him over there!'

'Over my dead body.' But in the end he did, so unnerved that he drove off the wrong way, back to the loading area, and there had been more screaming and yelling and anxiety.

They had had a miserable time. Everywhere they went they were followed by young lads.

'Mister, Missus, you take me and my brother, we show you best shop, you come, you come.'

In the end, despite his protests, she'd settled on a tall boy who looked like a young Paul Newman and his younger brother. Sure enough, they were very good guides, patient and informative and eager to please. They carried the shopping to a very respectable looking café and offered to mind it.

'No,' she'd said. 'Come in and have something.'

But they'd shaken their heads shyly and were waiting when they emerged.

Nothing better to do, I suppose, she thought, and later, sitting in a little park for a rest, she had asked the young Paul Newman, who said his name was Mohammed, how many languages he spoke. He said seven. By this time he and his brother had been joined by other young boys but somehow it was no longer oppressive.

'I'm hungry,' HE said, and they searched for a restaurant, the boys chattering and pointing this way and that. HE walked on ahead, puffing at his pipe.

'Vic!'

'What is it?'

HE came stumping back.

'I don't feel like it.'

'What do you mean?'

'I'm not hungry.'

She had suddenly felt strange. Not the weird moods she had experienced earlier when they first settled in Spain, feelings of unreality, of homesickness, of incapacity. It was something else. Something she couldn't put her finger on. It made her feel so odd that she leaned against the wall for a moment, giving him a fright.

'It's all right.'

She knew what it was. It was these boys.

She said to Mohammed, 'Don't you go to school?' and he shook his head.

She stood there, gripping her handbag. She, May, the oldest, with two young brothers – Phil, who had been a blue baby and who had been passed 'A1' by an army doctor in 1943 and had died in the African desert. Here, on this continent. And Tim, asthmatic, who had slipped away one winter's evening just before his ninth birthday.

'Vic, I feel so sorry for these lads.'

'Whatever for? What are you talking about, don't encourage them.'

She said, 'Give me the keys, I'll sit in the car. You can eat over there, that looks a good place.'

'Aren't you coming?'

'No, I'm feeling a bit queasy. You go on.'

He'd stood for a long moment, waiting for her to give in, and then had plodded off across the road. What a day. They had been advised to bring the car, and had hardly used it. There would be a week of moaning.

She opened her bag. Earlier she had asked him for some dirhams but he had paid for the little rug and the pots and dishes so she'd spent nothing of her float. She took out her purse and the boys, eyes wide, clustered round her. She dropped the money into the little brown palms. It was the younger brother who noticed that she was crying and nudged the slender Mohammed.

'Why do you cry?'

'You remind me of my brothers. When they were young.'

'Where are they now?'

'They're dead.'

His eyes, like so many of them, slightly crossed, in his case making him all the more handsome, flickered briefly and returned to her purse. She handed out more, pressing it into his hand.

'Share it out.'

'This is too much.'

'Share it.'

From nowhere more boys appeared, pushing and shouting at her. She stepped off the pavement into the road, holding her purse upside down. The group fell away. In the end, there was only Mohammed and his little brother, clutching his money with a dazed smile. She turned towards the car. Mohammed followed.

'No, I haven't anything else.'

He looked at her gravely.

'I come as your escort. I am your man.'

And she had sat in the car with the tears rolling down her cheeks and Mohammed on guard.

Mrs Frampton looked out of the window at the dripping vine leaves.

It must be the weather that's making me feel like this.

She had already tidied the bedroom, rearranged his things on the wardrobe shelves and ironed three shirts. She would put on the lamb. It was better done slow and there were the potatoes and the onions to peel.

After that there seemed nothing. She had finished her book, read *Woman* from cover to cover, and HE was out so there was no one to bicker with.

I am in a state.

There was nothing left but to scrub the kitchen floor.

That evening the sun came out. The air was like silk and they decided to try a restaurant.

'Never mind the lamb, we can have that tomorrow. Let's go to Puerto Banus.'

He liked going there. She didn't, it was too full of pretty girls who made her feel jealous, and handsome boys she couldn't take her eyes off, and all of them enjoying themselves, as she wasn't. It rubbed it in. But he liked the port. Although he kept his own boat at a cheaper marina he liked to walk along the trots in his silly cap looking at the yachts, passing judgment on seventy-foot schooners, commending an occasional plutocratic hull as a useful craft. To an onlooker you would suppose he had been round the world twice.

Oh well . . . if it makes him think he's got clocks on his socks.

After forty years of machine shops he had more than paid his subs. She went up to change into something decent.

Puerto Banus was full of people and noisier than ever.

'Let's eat here,' she said daringly, stopping at Romano's. This was where all the snobs and celebrities ate, where you sat to be seen. They chose a decorous table under a palm where the scent of damp jasmine flowers lay heavy on the air. It was expensive, Romano's, but the food was delicious and didn't sit on your stomach. The waiters were friendly but not familiar and nothing was hurried. You could sit there all night and they would refill your coffee cup without a hint or a look. She began to relax, pleased that she had put on the navy linen. It had cost enough, but what was the point of keeping it for a special occasion that might never happen. She touched the pink scarf at her neck, a present from Chloe. If only Michael weren't so far away. And why was that?

I'll never forgive you.

She looked at him sourly as he puffed his pipe. He'd never given that boy a day's chance, a moment's praise.

Thank God I was there.

Mike had survived, just. But it's made me mean, she thought to herself. We had to build a secret society in our own home. Thank God for Chloe, who was like Mum, who only saw the sun and was like a bubbling stream of life in the house.

Yes. It was fine.

She picked up a menu.

I feel like one of the crowd tonight. Which was unusual. Where she'd come from you soon learned that you weren't. That you weren't the thing, that you didn't belong, that you were rubbish, only tolerable if you kept quiet and did as you were told. They'd been behind the times out in the country, but there was evidence back home that these times were coming back. It made her murderous. She had helped Mum clean the big houses. She had marvelled at the carpets and the pictures and the ornaments . . . the hot water, the cars, the chandeliers. She remembered the scent of the massed flowers, game in the larder, biscuits in silver tins. Mum had looked and she had looked and never once had she been offered so much as an orange from a bowl.

And now here she was in the middle of the sun society among the tatty titles and the girls on the make, the lechers and the buyers and sellers. Mrs Frampton drank back her sherry and lifted her head in a short bark of laughter.

'What's up?'

'Nothing. I'll have another sherry, I think. And I'm going to have the lobster tails and the steak tartare.' This to the young fawn of a waiter at her elbow. 'And take the bread away, and the butter. We shan't be needing those.'

If you were going to put on the style, you might as well kick off right.

Chapter 4

H E HAD THE squits first and then she got them.
No question, mine's worse than his, though you'd never
think so. She was still carrying trays of rice and weak tea into
the bedroom between agonizing bouts.

It's a wonder my bottom doesn't fall off, thought Mrs
Frampton, washing her hands for the umpteenth time. She
couldn't find a clean towel and, weak, dried her hands on her
cotton skirt. His had only lasted a day and a half. Hers was in
the third day, without sign of remission. And HE was still
talking of calling the doctor. For himself.

When she looked in he had nodded off so she came away
with the bowl of semolina. She tried to eat it but, like
everything else, it tasted of tin. She put down the little blue
dish and found that she was crying.

'May, for heaven's sakes, whatever's the matter with you?'

She felt so low. What was she doing here? In this hot,
foreign country? The people were all right, she liked them. But
they weren't her people. She missed her friends, Phyl and
Noddy and Jean. They had said they would come and stay, but
would they?

Mrs Frampton let out a soft wail. Where was her mother?
She wanted her mum, her dear mother, who had suddenly
faded and gone within a month, taking the sun and the moon
with her. Nothing was right. She reached for one of the madras
napkins as mucus ran down the side of her mouth, and blew
forcefully. Come on. Enough was enough. It was no good
giving way. She was tired. All the changes, the selling up, the
move, finding a house, spending so much money. She
marvelled again at the way HE had let her have her head over
the furniture. He must have a fair bit stashed away. The
money's there, all right. He still wouldn't say how much they'd

got for the business. But she had a good idea. She hadn't kept his books all those earlier years without learning something.

He'll see me right, I suppose. She twisted the napkin. But what about the kids? Chloe had managed to get round him occasionally. Not often. But Michael? She shook her head and the tears vanished abruptly as bitterness invaded. What was the use of his money? Michael was gone. He wouldn't come back. He had his degree, he was doing well in Australia.

He'll not be back for his father's bit of brass.

And she smiled, thinking of her son, of the thick hair on his crown, giving him a tufted look just like her dad. His cracky voice, the long, awkward legs, the sharp nose. A teasing boy, with his clear eyes. All worthwhile for the kids, for Michael, and for Chloe with her shining eyes and her clear, sane, mocking intelligence.

Of course, she should never have done it. Who could you tell? Me? I gave my life away for a moment of jealousy.

Renee Richards.

So often the name came to her from nowhere. And in dreams. Renee Richards, from the same class as her, standing in the foyer of the dance hall, and picking up Mrs Frampton's left hand and waggling it, 'Hullo, May, still not got off yet?' and twisting the wedding ring on her own hand with a smirk, as Alan, dark Alan whom Mrs Frampton had watched and waited for, came up, smiled, and took Renee tenderly by the arm. And she had turned away, and plodded home with Vic that same night. And when he'd asked her to the pictures on the Sunday, instead of saying what she should have done, 'No thanks, I'm going out,' she had said yes, to be seen out with somebody, even if it was one of the stodgy Framptons.

She had never liked him, his shining skin, gravestone teeth. He smelt funny, and had nothing whatever to say to her. Once, after he'd waited in the rain for her under the sycamore, drips dripping on his bike for more than an hour, she'd had a moment's pang of feeling. Wet and speechless, even HE had looked romantic. She'd wondered if perhaps, after all, the silence hid something . . . shyness or panic. But realised soon enough that he was like the rest of his family, a closed shop.

Self-satisfied and without question. Nonetheless, despite herself, she had said yes when his mother had asked her to tea. That was the way of it then. People got excited, pushed you into it. And all to get a silly ring.

And what a disappointment that had been. She had expected that they would go together, choose – she had already picked out a dear little cluster. Instead, at the next Sunday tea, there it was, waiting for her on the sideboard, in a grey cardboard box. She'd had to get up in front of them all and squeeze past his father, who went on eating tinned peaches and bread and butter, to find a minute, ugly zircon, chosen, she'd found out, by his mother.

Never mind. I soon lost it.

What a laugh, she thought savagely. And the wedding! It would take till Doomsday to make the peace.

But there had been Michael, and the nurses rubbing her back through the pains and Mum gazing into the cot.

'Oh, our May, we've got Tim back, it's our little Tim.'

And then Chloe, born so fast she'd hardly had time to get the bus to the hospital for ten lovely days of rest and being waited on. And neither of them with any of Vic in them at all, no surliness, no picking on anything that wasn't tied to making money, no sneering at books and pictures, making fun of what they didn't understand.

If he was only *something* . . . religious, anything . . .

But to live with an empty bubble of vacated space, with someone who always lived in the past, in the future, never now, who had no thoughts, no ideas, no opinions. At least he'd had Michael educated.

I'll give him that.

He'd let him go to university, hard as it had been to wave the boy off with a smile, feeling the emptiness left behind.

Her bowels contracted in an awful spasm and she just made it to the lavatory as he bellowed from the bedroom.

'May? What are you up to?'

'What do you think?'

She squatted with difficulty on the bidet after, the bidet which she had called the duvet by mistake at the poolside,

23

giving them all a laugh. Why did they have to make them so low? You couldn't get up. Still, they were hygienic. She reached for the Savlon.

On the terrace, her stomach sore, she watched the swifts wheeling and dipping and tried a few steps down the path. What a tussle it had been! In the end she'd come straight out with it. He had his golf and the sailing club; she was going to spend on the garden, she'd go without clothes rather than not plant up properly. Mum had always looked after the garden at home. She'd grown flowers among the vegetables, making the neighbours laugh, and she and Dad would clamp up potatoes and carrots and pick over the apples in the loft together.

We knew how to do things then.

No, he couldn't begrudge her her patch.

She stood there smiling. It was more than a patch. Her smile broadened as she remembered yet again her first enquiries on the same spot, her tentative questions to the pueblo salesman. And his assurances that the rough piece of ground abutting the new house could be nicely landscaped for their convenience. And, to her own surprise, hearing herself pipe up like Lady Muck, 'Oh, no. I shall want that piece of land for a garden.' And the amazement when the salesman, without drawing breath, had agreed, a solution confirmed with enthusiasm by the moist-eyed Señor Ortega in the estate office.

HIS face! It had been like a battlefield, but in the end he had not been able to resist such a bargain. He had contented himself with grumbling all the way back to the *pensión* in the taxi.

'I'm not spending a fortune on useless plants.'

But she had dug in her heels.

Numero Uno, Calle Favoridad, Pueblo La Jolla, San Pedro de Alcantara . . . it still gave her pleasure to say the address to herself.

She shuffled down the garden path looking for signs of ants in the orange trees and puffs of whitefly in the mint underneath. Everything grew! Quicker than in a conservatory at home, so long as you watered. But the bugs grew as well. She bent queasily to nip off a dead marigold and had to lean against the olive tree. She took a few deep breaths. No, it had to be a bargain for him. There were people like that. They had to beat you, put one over. After all the work at Arlingford Road, painting and scraping, creating a garden from a rubbish dump on her own. Just as she'd made somewhere decent for the children to play and bring their friends, it had been up stumps to Bradford to that narrow house with the high, dark rooms with no garden nor outlook.

Then all the showing off as the business got bigger – having to be on tap all the time with the drinks tray ready – my God, didn't they knock it back! All those people chewing away at her table, never knowing who he was going to bring in.

'It's business!'

Until one day she'd gone on strike and threatened to walk out. After that he'd taken to restaurants. It suited them both. They met only at breakfast and then HE was out of it, leaving her and the kids at the table laughing and gossiping. And later Mike would arrive on his motor-bike from college, ravenous and teasing, with a bunch of violets and something for Chloe, and they would sit and discuss his future after finals.

Yes. I have all that. I have the children.

She remembered the clear April morning, with Hitler the cat clawing at her heels for food, when he told her gently that whatever job he took, whatever course his life might take, that it would have to be away from Bradford. She remembered the silence. And that he had grabbed her hand.

'Come to London, Mum. There's nothing for you and Chloe here.'

And she'd said, bald for once in her disloyalty, sick at heart at his announcement of leaving, 'I know. I'm no use to him, I don't know why he hasn't traded me in for a newer model.'

'Oh, you won't get rid of him that easily. You're good value. He'd miss you, all right.'

It was true. He'd hung onto her for the same reason that she'd been picked out with the cheap zircon engagement ring in the first place. They'd had it all worked out, his family.

They knew I cooked and gardened, made my own clothes. They knew we did our own bottling and pickling and preserving . . . we even mended our own shoes. I was a bargain.

*

The sun was hot and hurt the right side of Mrs Frampton's head. Oh God, it was coming on again. She scurried up the path in her slip-ons. The toilet flushed as she made the dining area and the relief of the shade.

'Are you in there?'

'What do you think?'

'Well, hurry up, I need to come in!'

She heard him grumble to himself as she bent over, grimacing with pain.

'Come on!'

What was he doing in there?

'Come *on*!'

There was a perceptible pause. She banged on the door. Silence.

'*Will* you come on!'

Another pause. Had he had a turn? Her mouth opened in alarm. The latch clicked. He came out, glaring.

'What's the matter with you?'

'I've got cramp!'

'Well, get in there then.'

As she doubled up in pain he pushed past her, knocking her against the wall. She heard the bedroom door click shut.

The mean so-and-so. He'd done it deliberately. She leapt for the lavatory but it was too late. The back of her slip soiled before she could squat. She leaned against the wall shaking with weakness, then sat on the pan, panting and miserable. Her bowels turned to water, the pain in deepening waves. Just hang on. No use getting upset. Let it ride over you. Things could be worse. Thank God HE hadn't got it this badly or there would have been an ambulance at the door and treks in the heat to the local hospital. She stretched out a weary hand.

He had used all the paper.

Chapter 5

THEY WERE STANDING in the parking area by the coach, waiting for the rest of the tour to come out of the gift shop. It had been a lovely morning, two gardens and a stop for lunch at a *parador*, one of the state-owned hotels. Before that there had been an unscheduled visit to a nearby vineyard with the result that most of the men and some of the women, including Kirsta, the quiet Danish woman, were now drunk. Kirsta was sleeping soundly on the back seat of the coach, covered by Mrs Frampton's cotton cardigan against the sun. This, the last stop, was at the local *vivero*.

'What do you want to see round a nursery for?' HE'd grumbled, keeping everybody waiting as he got out. It was a pity HE wasn't laid out on the back seat. He followed her round the rows of bougainvilleas and rose trees.

'You've not got room to put anything else in.' It was a fight that never ceased between them, the money Mrs Frampton dared to spend on her garden.

'Oh well,' she said, automatically picking off a leaf with black spot, 'perhaps next time they'll take us round a boat yard.'

I bet I don't spend as much as him on that wretched motor boat. Not as though we go anywhere! Serves him right. She grinned to herself. HE had been sold, rather than bought the boat as a way of popping over to Gibraltar and back. For several months they had gone to Gibraltar once a week. He couldn't stay away, and even spoke of living there. The border had been closed for many years but a local boat made a twice-weekly trip which, though technically illegal, no one seemed to mind. Livings needed to be made. So, every week she made her list and bought white sliced bread, Danish bacon pack, Sandwich Spread and his pipe tobacco. His new boat, the

Cecilia, was supposed to take over this run. But then the border had been opened again and you could go to Gibraltar legally, by car.

Not that HE would have taken to the water on his own. In a way, he was saved by the bell, let off the hook. At least it got him out of the house. Her Aunt Pearl had married a sailor. Buck, they called him, though his name was John. For a while after the Navy he'd been a paid hand on the Duke of Westminster's yacht. He'd settled down after Auntie Pearl had had the twins.

I wonder what happened to Nick and Tom, thought Mrs Frampton, her thoughts idling. Ginger twins, that had given the family something to talk about. Auntie Pearl, too, the flighty one, who'd worked in Woolworth's and worn red nail varnish. And then ginger twins.

'Glad it's not me,' they'd all said. But heads were never out of that pram.

The driver came out smiling. He had been filling up with beer and *tapas* at the bar. At first Mrs Frampton had not taken to *tapas*, the Spanish bits and pieces you ate with your drink or cup of coffee. She'd been wary of the little dishes of food, often fish, lying about on the counters. Bound to give you a stomach. But she'd had a go, in time. First the Spanish omelette, stuffed with diced potato, you could make a meal of that. Then other mixes, with tomato and onion, usually very fresh, and everywhere different, not like home, egg and chips, ham and chips, sausage and chips. She'd even tried chopped-up octopus, though only to annoy HIM. He never touched any of it. Occasionally, if there were *fritas*, potato crisps, he would munch his way through a packet . . .

'Come on, give us one,' she would say, but he would jerk away the packet, furious that she was filling her face with foreign muck and not taking his word that she was bound to be ill and cost him doctors' bills. When the terrible saga of death and illness from tainted cooking oil happened he never failed to quote every reference in the newspapers.

'If Spain's so bad, why did you come, then?' she would say, but of course, never got an answer.

Two of the Frenchwomen approached, snickering as usual. One of them had bought a lamp, a hideous swan that looked as if it had had its neck wrung. Señor García emerged and put on his sunglasses, almost bumping into her.

'Pardon,' said Mrs Frampton, and he hopped back and round her with a little bow. She wondered how he was getting on with his wife gone. He had a son and a daughter but they lived in the north, in Galicia, so the Frenchwomen said.

Mrs Frampton walked over to inspect a strawberry barrel. It looked a treat, the nice, fat terracotta pot with the plants already growing away all round the sides.

I've always wanted to try that.

The *vivero* man approached, short and swarthy.

'*Cuánto es, por favor?*'

'Two thoussan fiy unreh,' said the *vivero* man, kicking the pot lightly. He stood, feet apart, looking from Mrs Frampton to the pot.

He looks strong.

Mrs Frampton liked gardeners. They could be bad-tempered, but they were not miserable in a mean way. It was just that they got used to being on their own, not having their thoughts interrupted. Dad had never had a lot to say. But sweet as a custard apple inside. The *vivero* man bent forward and nipped off a leaf. The trouble with strawberries was they got the virus. You had to renew the stock all the time.

'Two thousand.'

She took the notes out of her pocket. Without pausing, he lifted the pot on his shoulder and walked off towards the coach.

Oh damn, and I've run out of film.

He would have made a lovely shot against the blue shutters and white geraniums of the house across the main road. The sturdy man and her lovely pot. But the pot was already descending into the boot of the coach. She watched him wedge it gently and firmly among the rugs, the wicker, the lamps and ornaments. As she was giving the *vivero* man his money HE came up.

Oh Law, thought Mrs Frampton, you would. Now spoil it for me.

'What's that . . . what's that you've bought?'

'Only something for the garden.'

'For the garden? What have you bought now, there's not a patch of earth to be seen as it is, I had to hack stuff from the bathroom window this morning, I couldn't see to shave.'

'You did what?' Furious, she turned away.

I know what you've done!

He'd taken the shears to her jasmine – just as the tendrils were really getting going. She'd been waiting for Miguel to turn up to tie them in for her with his ladder.

'Blow you, you sod.'

She shook her head at her own bad language. He *knew* she hated him to touch anything in the garden. She pulled a face.

Never mind. It'll grow again. He'll not stop it.

'What is it? What have you got?'

And his eye fell on the strawberry barrel.

'Eeh!' he said. 'Eeh!'

'It's a strawberry barrel. We'll get quite a crop off that.' He was fond of strawberries.

'Never.'

'We will. Look how everything grows here.'

'Eeh,' he said, and stood looking down at the pot. He even forgot to ask how much.

The driver tooted his horn. As Mrs Frampton moved forward, the *vivero* man returned, approaching without hurry. He was carrying three small pots and thrust them into Mrs Frampton's hands, jerking his head towards the back of the bus, and speaking in harsh, ejaculatory Spanish, the way they did.

'Ah, you mean they're replacements, for any that might die?' She said in her careful Spanish, 'You are saying that if a plant does not prosper . . . '

Clutching the plants to her left bosom she held out her hand and had it shaken violently.

On the bus HE was already seated, with the Dutchman. Mrs Frampton, her hands full of plants, made her way to the only free space at the back where the Danish lady was still flat out.

I'll have to move her legs.

She pushed them back gently so that she could sit down.

The Danish woman made no sound. There was a smell of sick. And something else. Something that Mrs Frampton, from her years of nursing, knew, felt, could smell a mile off.

The pots fell off her lap.

'Stop the bus.'

People turned round.

'This woman's dead,' said Mrs Frampton.

It was useless. She did all the things she knew. But she'd seen it before. The woman had inhaled vomit. She was dead, asphyxiated. The police came, and the ambulance, and they all got out and waited, it seemed for hours, in the sun. It was ages before, shocked and silent, they reached the pueblo. Mrs Frampton couldn't take it in. Kirsta? The restrained, inoffensive Danish lady? Who lived so sensibly in her apartment with her embroidery and her pictures of her children?

That's the second death in the pueblo this year. And both women.

She was depressed for weeks. And angry with guilt. Why hadn't she kept an eye on Kirsta? Why hadn't she noticed, before it was too late? She took to shopping and window-gazing, and going for long and exhaustive walks on her own. She even sat with the Frenchwomen by the pool, finding their abrasiveness more sustaining than the sad glances of most of the other residents.

It was those bloody strawberries. If I hadn't stopped to buy those strawberry plants . . .

And they died. Every one. She watered them regularly and got Miguel to move the pot to a shadier corner. The extra three were put in as replacements until in the end only one plant remained, growing strongly out of the top. It's not meant, she thought and, serving dinner one night, said, 'I'm fed up with that strawberry pot. I'm going to put it in the local auction.'

'All dead, are they?'

'All but one.'

After they had eaten they put on the patio lights and went to have a look.

'I could try something else, I suppose. I could plant some

convolvulus and let it trail down the sides. Out you come!' And she yanked at the strawberry plant.

'Don't do that!' he bellowed, making her jump. He snatched the plant away from her.

'Nothing wrong with this, perfectly good plant, what did you want to go and do that for?'

'I'm fed up with trying. Besides, it was the day we lost Kirsta. It reminds me.'

'All the same – '

'Throw it away.'

'I'll not.'

'What are you going to do with it?'

'What do you think? Plant it!'

'Where?'

'I'll find a spot. They want the right spot. Get a whole patch out of this one. They spread.'

What do you know, she thought to herself. But she was pleased. Surely he wasn't going to take to gardening. They argued violently over the siting. He wanted the strawberry on the patio.

'There isn't room, besides, there's not enough light.'

Then he wanted to put it among her gazanias.

'You'll upset my colour scheme!'

They settled on a minute patch of dappled shade under the peach tree.

The strawberry plant did well. It put out a couple of suckers and they too thrived and the plant itself came into flower. She surprised him taking a photograph of it. His hand shook with pleasure so the picture was blurred. Still, it was recognisable as a strawberry.

Wonders will never cease, thought Mrs Frampton. The memory of Kirsta and her cushions with the speedwells and buttercups, her runner with the dog roses, her big dinner cloth with the poppies and ears of corn edged into her thoughts now and then. And always associated with the strawberry barrel (now alive with nasturtiums) and the last sturdy strawberry plant. The survivor. It made Mrs Frampton pensive.

I don't see why Kirsta had to go. She wasn't a drinker. She

liked her food – well, so do I.

And Mrs Frampton pondered on the nature of accident. It never made sense. All those children brought into casualty, burned, faces contorted with poison, crushed, broken, swollen. And she and her mates had had to wash, to straighten out, to make the best of what was left for the parents to see. Heavens, the things they'd done . . . putting bits together after a gas explosion, then running with the bits to make another whole shape for another shocked, grey-faced family . . . well, what could you do? At least with Kirsta it had been quick. She probably hadn't suffered.

'You know what?' he said, shuffling heavily into the kitchen in his new moccasins. 'We've got one!'

'One what?'

'What do you think? A strawberry!'

Yes, she thought, and when it was really bad and you'd lost a patient after a hard fight, after surgery and that blessed relapse . . . some people just didn't know how to fight . . . or when some wretch of a gossiping surgeon had nicked a vein and you had to cover up . . . those were the times she crept into the nursery to look at all the new ones. The live ones. Successfully delivered, the student nurses armed with bottles to keep the little devils quiet so that the mothers, tucked up for the night, could get rest and recovery. Not like now, she thought grimly, when they tip you out and send you home the next day and you have to pretend to be Superwoman. To suit them. Ten days it used to be. She would sit in there taking her turn with the babies and hoping that when her time came it would be twins . . . two for the price of one like Auntie Pearl.

'How long before it's ready for eating?'

'Oh, Lord knows,' said Mrs Frampton, her mind elsewhere.

'I thought you were supposed to know about gardening.'

'This is Spain. Things are different here.'

After he'd gone off to the links she went out to have a look. He was right. There *was* a little strawberry there. It was small and green, but glinting with pips, already quite recognisable.

Well, Kirsta, she thought, you're on your way again.

Chapter 6

THERE WAS A roaring bellow from the back patio, making her jump.

'May!'

'What?'

'Was it you?'

'What?'

'Did you eat it?'

'Eat what?'

'The strawberry!'

'No!'

'You must have done!'

'Well, I didn't.'

HE came and stood in the open doorway, his shadow making it impossible to sew.

'You must have.'

She put down her cushion cover. 'I haven't eaten your strawberry, don't be so silly.'

'You must have.' And he pushed past her and marched off down the new crazy paving.

Mrs Frampton sucked in her teeth. Honestly. She followed him down the path.

'It wasn't me.'

He turned, his one precious quiff of hair rising in the breeze like the arm of the Lady in the Lake.

'Who was it, then?'

'How should I know?'

'You were out here this morning, I saw you. I said to you – I told you yesterday it would be ready today – '

'I've already said – it wasn't me!'

'Then who was it?'

Mrs Frampton, finding the sun too much for her, came back

to the sanctuary of the dining area under the shade of the vine.

'*I* don't know.'

He stood over the precious plant, seeking its message. His behind, in the loose grey worsteds, bulged, offending Mrs Frampton and making her spiteful.

'You probably ate it yourself.'

'Don't be more stupid than you are.'

'You were drunk enough.'

'When?'

'Last night.'

'I never came out here last night.'

'Yes you did. After we put the car away. When we came back from Len and Sybil's.'

'We came in the other way.'

'You said you wanted a beer. You went through, the next thing you had all the patio lights on, and there you were bending over and talking to it.'

'It's been plucked straight off. You can see! The stalk's still there.'

It went on all morning, all through the spaghetti bolognese and the fruit salad.

'Oh, come on, Vic, for Heaven's sakes. Not as though it's something rare – they're cheap enough, strawberries, in the market.' Well, not cheap, nothing was cheap any more.

'That's not the point. I don't understand it! Nobody else has been here!'

'Perhaps it was a bird.'

'Oh yes?' he said, with heavy sarcasm. 'So a bird's plucked it clean off, in one?'

'It could. Well, a big bird. A big bird would.'

'What big bird? We haven't seen any big birds. We haven't seen any little birds, let alone big birds.'

It was true. Apart from a lone egret, and a few boring, chattering sparrow-like birds, they'd seen none. Mrs Frampton, who had expected exotic plumage and strange beaks among her rapidly growing foliage, had complained to the Frenchwomen, who knew everything. They had shaken their heads without interest but Mrs Miller, usually shy, had whispered, 'They eat them.' There had been nods all round. The gypsies, said the girl married to the Spanish discothèque manager, trapped all the birds in the hills behind the town and sold them, or made them into stew.

'We used to have rook pie when I was a kid,' Mrs Frampton had said.

'Well, I don't know.'

He followed her into the lounge and sat with a morose expression, watching her stitch up the hem of her skirt.

'It's no use looking at me. I haven't had your strawberry. If I want strawberries I can go and buy them for myself, I don't have to go raiding them off you, thank you very much.' His voice modified, taking on the whine of a boy at his mother's elbow. She knew what it meant. He wanted, he needed her to solve the mystery for him. She bit off her thread and said, 'It could have been the Dutchman.'

'When?'

'When he brought the table.'

'Never. What would he do that for?'

'He might, after lumbering in with a piece of furniture in the heat. Probably looked down on the way out, saw a nice strawberry – '

'It was decent size and all – '

'He's a greedy sort, look at his stomach and the way he was knocking it back when we were looking round the shop.'

'He came in the other way. Through the front. He couldn't have done it.'

Mrs Frampton flicked a glance at his resentful back. Bother. Now he would moan all day. Rats. She needed him to go with her to the auction. There was a small blue and white plaque with the head of boy on it, but she didn't fancy going alone. It was a small auction in the basement of a shop, run by a tall Spanish man and his Italian wife. They made jokes in different languages and kidded people into buying. It put her off. With him beside her they were left alone. Nobody made a joke when he was around.

'Look,' she said, in a placating voice, 'I dare say it was young Manolo from next door.'

'Thieving little – '

'Now, Vic . . . ' She wasn't having him swearing in her sitting-room.

'What do you want to let him in here for?'

'I like him, he's a nice little kid.'

'Too sharp for his own good.'

'I can practise my Spanish.'

'You shouldn't let him in.'

She picked up her thimble. There was a moment's peace, and then, 'Anyway . . . didn't you say they'd all gone to Ronda for the weekend?'

Damn.

'So it couldn't have been him. Come on, May, out with it! Just so long as I know. So long as I know who it was, where it went, I don't mind so much.' That was a good one.

'I've told you. I haven't touched your strawberry.'

He got up and went out to the front hall. She heard him pick up the telephone.

'Gottfried? Hullo, how are you today?'

There was a long discussion of the previous morning on the golf course. Good. That was better. She put her sewing away and changed into her sandals. And then, just as she was cheering up, came the bellow again.

'Don't tell me! We've had them in this area too. They've been at my strawberries – cleared the lot!'

It was just as well that the friendship was a golfing one, she thought to herself. The German lived on the other side of Calahonda and they only met on the links. It's as well he can't see the size of your strawberry patch, you old show-off. Come on, make yourself useful, Gottfried, thought Mrs Frampton irritably, but the conversation seemed to be getting more and more savage as the collapse of law and order since the death of Franco came round for the umpteenth time. Trust him to pick a German for a buddy. They were both getting well steamed up, she could even hear the guttural squawks from the other end.

'You're right, Gottfried . . . I couldn't agree with you more – no sense to it at all!' And the receiver was banged down with a crack.

'Mind the bakelite!'

'I'm going out.'

That meant no car for her. And no auction. She listened to him crash his clubs out of the hall cupboard . . .

Oh yes, and if I banged the paintwork like that, I'd be for it. That was that, then. Bother and damnation. The blue plaque gleamed in her mind, for ever out of reach.

It hadn't even tasted very nice, as strawberries went. A bit sharp.

Chapter 7

'DID IT SAY ten-thirty?'

'You know it said ten-thirty. Typical.' He banged his glass on the café table and the waiter came obediently. 'Beer . . . a beer!'

'*Una cerveza*,' said Mrs Frampton, remembering her *seseo* and pronouncing it 'thervetha', but the waiter had already gone and HE gave her his usual look with the sneer and glare combined. Yes, she thought, I know you resent the money spent on my Spanish classes, but where would we be without them? She thought with complacency of the mess with the telephone, and the fuss with the roof, and giggled aloud at the memory of their new young bank manager, who had asked HIM for a few tips, confessing that his previous job had been in a travel agency. His face!

They sipped their drinks, making them last. A few people went by. There was no sign of the parade. The tubular crowd barriers were in place, but where were the crowds?

'It's the right week, any road,' said Mrs Frampton, 'Passion Week, I know that.'

'Eh?'

'The week before Easter Sunday . . . anyway, it's all in there.' She pointed to the copy of the *Marbella Times* on the table between them. 'It said ten-thirty p.m., Tuesday, the parade of hoteliers and Saint Marta.'

'Who?'

'Saint Marta.' She opened the paper. 'There you are . . . there it is, in print.' He had a touching faith in anything that was put in the paper. A large Spanish family surged by, knocking his chair. 'Vic!' she said, as he swore. Father, mum, three little boys, grandmother, grandad, all jostling and nudging and laughing. She felt a lurch of loneliness deep in her belly.

'Is that a band?'

'I think you're right.'

They walked up the cobbled steps and across the little square with the *banco* that was covered in pink geraniums, and on up one of the narrow streets, pausing to listen. 'It's nearer.'

But then the sound seemed to be further away. Mrs Frampton's veins began to hurt.

'I said we should go up to the church.'

'I'm not going all that way.'

But he followed her, puffing and grunting. As they turned into the alley by the garden with the arum lilies there was a sudden burst from the band, much closer now. The sound was a mess, there must be two bands. Plenty of people now in the narrow passage ways, all laughing, talking and eating peanuts, children pushing through, young couples arm in arm. When they got to the church square they could see the white hoods of the penitents over the heads of the crowd.

'Is this all?' HE was behind her, the smell of his pipe more acrid than usual. There were only five penitents, and the hood of one of those hung down instead of piercing the ink-blue night sky like the others. 'Ran out of starch.' Mrs Frampton laughed to herself at her own joke. Everywhere you looked, people looked into your eyes, looked back at you. It was embarrassing at first but then she began to like it. It was as though you all knew one another. Everybody was happy, excited . . . even the men. And then the big doors of the church opened, scattering the band. And out came the float.

'Oh, Vic!' said Mrs Frampton.

It was huge. Like a massive oblong boat, but curved and gilded, trimmed with cream and silver, a bit like Frascati's in the old days. On the corners were arrangements of lilies and carnations, maroon, crimson and pink.

'Oh, it's lovely!' And a German woman beside her said, 'Yah, yah,' and smiled.

Mrs Frampton looked up, standing on tiptoe to see the figures. First there was Christ. He was thin and handsome, with a sad, frightened look on his face. By Gum, whoever did that caught him, she thought; that's Jesus Christ, all right, to the life! Behind him was an angel, kneeling, with a wobbly halo and arms held up – nice, sturdy, short arms – and, behind, the angel Saint Marta, a pleasant-faced woman carrying a tray with a flask of wine and a goblet.

'Look, Vic!'

'What? I can't see a damned thing.'

'We'll cut through to the bottom, they'll have to go that way.' He looked dubious. 'Come on, might as well get our money's worth.'

He turned obediently and she followed him along the little side street. As he bent forward to take the slope, he looked suddenly very old. She called ahead, 'Not if it's too much. We can go back to the car if you want.' But he seemed not to hear and she followed him across the main square with the scent from the orange trees filling the air. Everyone had the same idea, and there was a squash, but she managed to keep him in sight, and as they squeezed past a parked lorry the procession came into view. Now there were a dozen penitents. They shuffled along casually, pulling at their hoods. 'Kids, most of them,' she whispered as he rasped for breath. 'Look at their feet.' Most of them were wearing sneakers. Their mothers might have put them into decent black shoes, it spoiled the effect. They followed the procession back to the main square, where everything came to a halt. He grunted, cleared his throat ominously.

'We'll be here all night.'

'All right. We'll go if nothing happens soon. This is Spain – *mañana*, remember!' She got a nasty look. And then, suddenly, the square was full of penitents, ten, fifteen, nineteen of them.

'I wonder if there are any women – under the hoods.'

'What?'

'I said . . . doesn't matter.'

She was having to shout because the noise from an approaching band was deafening. Another band! The penitents shambled off, trailing long white candle holders, and into the square marched a band of young lads in dark green jackets, with white plastic cuffs, white belts and straps . . . and white

Nazi helmets. What's more, they were goose-stepping. 'Leave it,' she snapped, as he started to rumble. As if he wasn't more Nazi than the Nazis! His flag-waving had always been a special irritant, especially as he had only been in the Catering Corps and never fired a rifle. He really thinks he's patriotic, she mused, watching the boys march off briskly to a drumbeat. Funny thing, patriotism. Excuse for a punch-up most of the time.

'I'm off. I'm going back to the car. How long are you going to be?' he bawled at her.

'I don't know. I want to see the parade!'

'Well, I'm not stopping.'

'Go on, then, take the car. I'll find my own way home.'

'Aye, by bloody taxi, I know that one.'

She wheeled and glared at him, lips pressed together.

'I'll walk!'

It was better with him gone. The band had stopped somewhere in the narrow lanes, you could hear the drums tapping, de derum, de de rum, de de rum, rum, rum. It began to go through her head, but then it stopped, and the sound of the starlings in the orange trees took over. And two women walked into the square.

'Eee!' said Mrs Frampton, aloud.

They were not young, either of the women. They wore black dresses, mid-calf, one with a ruffled collar, the other with a bodice draped to one side. Both wore fine black stockings and winkle pickers, and high tortoiseshell combs with *diamanté*, and huge mantillas floating away behind. They carried rosaries, and one had a prayer book with a mother of pearl cover. Both of them wore a lot of make-up, mascara, dark red lipstick and blue eyeshadow.

Well, thought Mrs Frampton. But the more she looked, the more entranced she was. They looked a treat! Grave, dignified, and absolutely sure of themselves. None of that kicked-dog look of the older Englishwoman, none of the 'excuse-me-for-living' apology of the British matron. And here were some more of them! One was very stout, then a tall fair woman of about forty, then a young one in a beautiful lacy dress with a

44

low neckline, then an elderly woman with a ravaged face and heavy bags under her eyes. But they *all* looked wonderful. What is it, she thought. How is it they *all* look so nice? It was partly the way they stood. These Spanish women knew how to stand up straight. The old one was wearing make-up and all. And looked like an empress. I must go in for more black, thought Mrs Frampton. I must try it in a different way. It usually made her look like a widow. It's to do with style – well, let's face it, you've never had that, May. They had it, these women, moving forward slowly glancing from side to side, acknowledging friends with slight nods, unselfconscious. Everything stopped once more. The women stood. Five, ten minutes went by. They seemed quite happy to stand and be looked at. No one seemed worried or impatient.

If it were me, I'd be going mad.

At last the procession moved off. Now there were more penitents still, their eyes glinting through the holes of their hoods. Some of the eyeholes were slitted and sinister, others round, even droopy, like basset hounds. And then the sound of another band, a big band, the town band, in blue and gold. And the float again, lurching across the square on the shoulders of twenty men with a crablike gait, odd and predatory. She could see the thin, pale, troubled Jesus very plainly now. And it made her mind flash back to the years of church and Sunday school, and thinking Well, I'm for hell, I can't believe in all this stuff about the Host and Hosannah and One in Three. As for all the stuff about blood, she'd soon seen too many Catholic women straining to birth too many babies, and the priests at the bedside muttering over them when they were pegging out – by God, if she'd ever let a man tell her what it was all about. The local priests were going by now, and then the Mayor, young and handsome, and the local soldiery and the police chiefs, a murderous looking bunch, though not bad looking. No, you could keep religion. It caused wars. As for that Pope, telling women what they could and couldn't do. What did he know about it? Come to think of it, he was handsome enough to know a bit too much. Pity the town band was trying Verdi, the trumpets weren't up to the top notes. She watched the last straggling penitents hopping off after the procession, their skirts in their hands.

To her surprise, HE was sitting in the car waiting for her, she'd almost not bothered to look. As she opened the door he said smugly, 'I've got a prime position, the whole thing comes this way.' He was parked parallel to the main road, but a little higher. They could look down over the heads of the crowd, unobstructed.

'I've seen it all,' she said, 'still, I don't mind watching it again.' They waited. Two policemen stood in the road in crepe-soled shoes, armed with truncheons and pistols. Both were smoking. Then a couple of little boys began to play in the middle of the road, weaving and dodging right under the feet of the police.

'They're for it.'

But the policemen took no notice . . . one, in fact, moved out of the way for the children to play.

'They wouldn't get away with that at home,' he muttered. An older policeman came up. The boys lurched into all three. Oh dear. But not one of the men turned his head. Beside her, she could feel him stiffen as she smothered a giggle.

They waited a good half an hour. Now it was Mrs Frampton's turn to get restless, and his to sit in triumph, refusing to move. But at last the penitents began to straggle into view. Now there were heaps of them! All their candles were lit in the beautiful twilight, and they waved them about recklessly, threatening to set fire to themselves. Then the goose-stepping band, now much larger, and now her ladies, rows and rows of them, tall and short, fat and thin, young and old, even one elderly imperious old girl being wheeled in a chair. She got out of the car and pushed forward, seeking to find one who looked a fool, looked a mess, looked out of place. There were slingbacks, court shoes, open-strap sandals, straight skirts, pleated skirts, long skirts, knee-lengths, capes, jackets, two-pieces, cocktail dresses. Even the fat ones looked dignified, stately, handsome and serene. When she got back to the car her legs felt on fire and her veins about to explode. He turned the car with difficulty as the dispersing crowds swirled past them, shouting and swearing.

'Vic, don't!'

It took them ages to get back. 'Cup of tea?' she said, but HE was already on the stairs. She heard the lavatory go, then the bathroom door. At the kitchen table she sat for a long time, till the tea got too strong and she had to thin it with hot water.

I wish we'd had things like that . . .

Oh I am a fool, it's all idol worship . . .

That poor Jesus . . .

I wonder how Gudrun got on . . .

Gudrun was her friend from the flower-arranging class. She had gone with a friend to see the processions in Jerez. When she came back on the Friday, Mrs Frampton gave her coffee and apple cake. Gudrun's procession sounded wonderful, four floats, penitents with blue velvet hoods and three bands.

'Puts ours in the shade,' said Mrs Frampton.

'In the shade?'

'Our parade was a bit of a shamble, though I enjoyed it. Yours sounds properly organised.'

'Oh yes,' said Gudrun happily, 'it was very nice. And children too, quite frightening and nice.' Her English wasn't sound.

On the Saturday the Frenchwomen came back from Seville. Of course, they'd seen the lot – bands dressed like Roman centurions, with real ostrich feathers, and all-night processions. Mrs Frampton, as usual, soon went quiet. They'll be on for days, she thought. I don't care. She heard how they'd taken a chance, and found a cancellation at the Hotel Macarena, and had seen the cathedral. They displayed the huge coloured cards they'd bought and Mrs Frampton was knocked out by these. The closeups of the Madonna's head affected her, the wooden, painted face, the warm pink cheeks, the moulded tears. And the floats! White candles, white flowers, silver floats, gold tissue dresses, everything so exotic that Mrs Frampton couldn't clear the pictures from her mind. She gazed helplessly at the closeup of the Madonna, at the expression on the idol's face, at the mixture of sense and shyness, sweetness and a sort of inward knowingness.

'I'd love one of these,' she heard herself saying.

'Alas, I think they are not on sale here. Only in Seville,' said Eliette, the tall Frenchwoman, grasping the cards swiftly.

Mrs Frampton had a flash of insight. 'Naturally, I'd pay for it.'

There was a swift conversation in French.

'Nine pesetas, for the larger. Two, if you wish.' She found herself buying two obediently. She would have liked the whole lot. Somehow, they weren't in the right hands. The Frenchwomen rose, still chattering, and went inside for aperitifs.

Oh, drat them.

She watched Gudrun come down the steps and join them at the bar. Now they'll be treading all over her trip. Well, if she preferred their company, it was up to her. She had her two pictures. Perhaps she could have them done in little gilt frames. A shadow crossed her face.

'Good day.' It was Gudrun.

'You seemed to be having a good laugh over there.'

'I like the orange juice. Mateo always gives a good big size.'

'You weren't on the aperitifs, then?'

'Ho, no, no!'

She showed Gudrun the pictures.

'Oh, but these are so beautiful!' Gudrun's eyes shone, and Mrs Frampton felt a sudden prick of tears. What a good sort Gudrun was, no spite in her at all, she put you to shame.

'I bought them from the French ladies, I fell in love with them,' she said. 'I'm afraid their trip puts our processions . . . '

'In the shade?' And they grinned at each other.

'Well,' said Mrs Frampton, 'Seville, umpteen bands, Roman legions, all-night dos . . . ' She looked at Gudrun who was sipping her orange. 'They always seem to go one better.'

'Yah.' And suddenly the little blue eyes swivelled towards Mrs Frampton and Gudrun smiled broadly, creasing up her broad nose.

'But not so fine, I'm thinking.'

'Oh?'

'They were sleeping in a corridor, with people walking. They got lost for three hours in the night in fog, and couldn't be finding the hotel. They couldn't see any of the parade, and the thin one got squashed.'

'Squashed?'

'It was narrow streets and many people. They are separated, and the little one gets hysterics, and then a policeman tells them the wrong direction, through drink. They are quite angry.'

Mrs Frampton smiled. And laughed. And shook her head.

'Ours was the best,' said Gudrun, licking the shreddy bits from the side of her glass.

The Frenchwomen were getting up and going inside to eat. As they went through the door she saw the tall one throw a big envelope into the café waste bin.

'Hang on,' said Mrs Frampton, and hurried across, surprised at her own speed. Yes. It was the big blue envelope with the cards. She picked it up, not caring who saw her, and looked inside. They were all here . . . she'd thrown them away, the pictures of the floats, of the Madonna, closeups, all of them! She brought them back to the table.

'I saw,' said Gudrun. 'She threw them out.'

They pored over the pictures, making their selections.

'The big one for you,' said Gudrun, 'you were the finder. And one more for me, yah?'

It had been a good sort of week.

Chapter 8

THEY OFTEN PASSED the house when they drove into the hills to eat at the Greek place. A white wall bordered the road for half a mile at least, and below the wall grew a ribbon of irises, beautifully tended with no dead leaves or overgrown lumpy bits.

'It's like Portugal,' Mrs Frampton had said, the first time they had driven that way. 'You remember . . . Gudrun, the Swedish lady, was telling us. The Portuguese employ gardeners, to garden the roadside, I think it's a good wheeze.'

But HE had only grunted. He was no gardener, never would be. When she did get him to touch anything it died.

From the top of the slope you could just see the roofs of the big, low house. It belonged to a Chinawoman, a Madame Liu.

'I didn't know they let them out, the Chinese,' Mrs Frampton had said to her friend, the deaf Mrs Miller.

'What?' Sally Miller had replied as usual and then, hearing late as she always did, had suggested over the coffee cups, 'Probably from Hong Kong. That's where all the money is.'

Madame Liu was reputed to be fabulously wealthy and to wear emeralds as big as eggs. Her name was often on the lists of trustees to charitable foundations, and she was said to give lavishly. Beyond that, nothing was known. She was seen little and the high, soft-blue-painted gates were never open. Mrs Frampton, when they drove that way, enjoyed the groves of flowering jacaranda and the feathery casuarina trees which rose above the long white walls, but soon thought little about the reclusive owner.

Until, one day, when she was walking along the beach for an early morning stroll, she heard a funny noise coming from the trees beyond the sand. There was a low, whining sound – at first she took it for some sort of machinery. She walked up the beach and paused. The sand here gave way to a mixture of sand and earth and pine needles and the bright green of oxalis, the shamrock that seemed to grow everywhere despite drought or shade. She cocked an ear, listening. A woman in a bikini, close by, sat up . . . the hotel was just beyond the rise and the gardens gave onto the beach. A short man in dark trousers and a linen jacket came down the steps briskly.

'What eesa eeta?' He sounded Italian, and advanced briskly on tiny feet.

'I don't know.' She moved in under the pines. The noise stopped, and then started again . . . a miserable, breathless moaning.

'Oh dear,' said Mrs Frampton, 'I think somebody's hurt.'

She walked forward, followed by the man, who called back, in English and then in Spanish, 'Get help. There has been an accident.'

The woman in pink advanced, together with a girl in blue, and a small man in minuscule red trunks. The sound continued. Mrs Frampton, ahead of the rest, called, 'Sssh!' The sound was very close now, and she could hear a faint rustle. A couple of waiters came bounding down the steps and across the undergrowth.

'No!' called Mrs Frampton. 'Shut up a minute.'

But the men, both young, plunged forward, and one of them shouted, 'Is nothing . . . *de nada* . . . it's a dog.' He turned and his brown, alive face was smiling. And dismissive. The pink woman turned away.

'Let me see,' said Mrs Frampton. She pushed through the low shrubby growth and bent down, the Italian leaning over her shoulder.

'Oh, *poverino*!'

'It's hurt.'

'Probably a car. It has crawled here to die. Leave it, *Signora*, please.'

Mrs Frampton straightened up. 'No, you can't do that.' But the Italian had already turned away.

He said to the taller waiter, 'Fetch something heavy. Quickly . . . this noise is not attractive for the guests. Get rid of it.'

Mrs Frampton said, 'I think it's only broken its leg.'

'Quickly,' said the man, and two other women who had strolled over to have a look nodded agreement, murmured sympathy, and moved off to dive into the swimming pool.

'No,' said Mrs Frampton. The waiter dithered, looking from her to the Italian.

'Oh, for heaven's sakes,' called the pink woman, 'put it out of its misery.' The smaller waiter approached with a spade.

Good God, thought Mrs Frampton, they're going to kill it.

She bent, to pick the dog up. The Italian man tried to push her away. She turned, furious, and pushed him back. He let out a stream of abuse and gestured angrily to the waiters, who almost knocked Mrs Frampton over.

'Don't you dare!' she shouted. 'Leave the dog alone, you devils . . . leave it alone, I say!' And she barged forward and picked the dog up, making it howl loudly. She stood, facing the three men.

The one with the spade came towards her. 'Please . . . *Señora*,' he said, with a would-be charming smile.

Mrs Frampton, having given the leg a swift glance, saw that although the bone was protruding, it was a clean, if slanting break. It would knit in no time. The dog was obviously a stray, and very thin. But young. It had its life ahead of it. She began to move off.

'*Signora*, what do you theenk you do?'

All three men advanced on her as she backed away towards the beach.

Suddenly, from behind Mrs Frampton, there came a strange little voice. High, almost like a child, but with a precision that had nothing of the childish in it.

'Leave this lady, please.'

Mrs Frampton turned, clutching the dog to her, and saw a tiny Chinese woman dressed in a cream linen suit with a small brimmed hat and bag to match. The waiters stepped back at once, bowing. The little woman came forward.

'The dog's leg is broken,' said Mrs Frampton. 'There's no need to kill it.'

'They are afraid that the hotel guests will be disturbed,' said the little woman softly.

'I'll disturb *them*,' muttered Mrs Frampton, and, to her surprise, the little woman giggled and put her hand over her mouth.

'We shall take him to the veterinary surgeon,' she said.

The two of them, the little woman hardly up to Mrs Frampton's shoulder, walked up the steps and through the hotel gardens, past the artificial streams and the heavy, flowering trees. Mrs Frampton, finding the dog heavy, soon panted some paces behind. By the third flight of steps, the little woman had disappeared, but when Mrs Frampton reached the large sandy parking area under the stone pines, there she stood, impeccable and smiling in the cream suit, in front of a very large, shining, dark blue Rolls-Royce saloon.

By heck, thought Mrs Frampton. She murmured as she puffed forward, 'I think you may have fallen on your feet, son.'

The dog, in her arms, wagged his tail slightly at the sound of her voice.

Two hours later they were driving through the gates of the Casa Morisca, the true name of the locally called Casa Peking, up the long winding drive to the low white house. Dwarfed trees in massive and ornate square pots graced the wide verandahs. Mrs Frampton, following the little Chinese lady and followed by the chauffeur gently bearing the dog, longed to pause before the beautiful, contorted almond trees with their translucent green leaves and pale pink blossoms. But she followed obediently through a wide portico and across a central court-yard. More trees . . . one, a dombeya, which Mrs Frampton, too, was trying to grow. So far, she'd been defeated by the way the large pink blossoms browned so quickly in the wind. Ah, the thing was to put it under shelter. This tree was perfect, pruned to a spreading, comely shape.

She was shown to a cloakroom by a Spanish maid and then, when she emerged, into a long salon looking west over a lake.

'How do you like tea?' asked the little lady, the maid at her elbow.

'Oh . . . you know.'

'English style?' And the little lady laughed, a tiny, tinkling sound that made Mrs Frampton laugh, too.

'Yes. Indian tea, quite strong, milk but no sugar – I've managed to give it up at last.'

'Yes. I, too.'

'Oh, but you've no need to, surely?'

'Better safe than sorry.' It was true. The R sounds did sound like L sounds, almost.

'I am May. May Liu.' And the little lady rose and held out her hand.

'I'm May, too. May Frampton.' And this revelation caused them both to stare, and pause. It was somehow significant. They smiled.

The long and the short of it, thought Mrs Frampton. Wouldn't do for us to be seen out together, we'd be mocked – still, no chance of that. Looking away to mask a smile she noticed a painting, a woman's head in greys and pinks and greens. Without thinking, she rose.

'Is this a Marie Laurencin?' The little May smiled and nodded.

'May I?' Mrs Frampton took a turn around the long room, gazing in wonder at paintings, aware of her bulk, but feeling no judgment, sensing even good will behind her. When she sat down again her eyes were wide.

'That Renoir!'

'Which do you like the best?'

'Oh, you can't compare. Though I suppose if I had to choose . . . for my birthday, say . . . I'd take the Matisse of the woman by the window.'

Little May made a soft, hissing sound. 'So would I.'

Tea, with tiny cream cakes, sent Mrs Frampton into a dreamy torpor. For a while, after the trays were removed, there was a comfortable silence. Then the little May said, 'Do you think that the dog has an owner?'

'No. His ribs are sticking out. He's a stray, but, like the vet said, healthy. He's a nice-looking dog.' She frowned, wondering if she dared . . . but no. HE'd have a fit.

She shook her head slightly, and Little May, as if answering her train of thought, said, 'He can stay with me. I have already five dogs, so one more . . . ' and they had another giggle.

'I'd love a dog, we always had dogs on the farm when I was a girl. My husband's not keen.' Little May looked at her, and away. She doesn't miss much, thought Mrs Frampton.

They went through to a large, comfortable kitchen, where two dalmatians rushed forward and a large mongrel lifted a paw.

'The terriers are out somewhere, digging up my flowers.'

Mrs Frampton, who had been expecting the usual ferocious Dobermans and Alsatians, smiled.

'He's a lucky chap,' she said, and bent down to tickle the invalid, now resplendent on cushions in a dog basket.

'You saved his life.'

'Oh no, I'd have got nowhere without your pull.'

'My pull?'

'Your authority.'

'We share the honour.'

At the door she laid a hand on Mrs Frampton's arm. 'You will come to visit the patient . . . and me?'

'I'd like that very much. I live in the Pueblo La Jolla.'

She wrote her telephone number on a creased piece of paper from her bag. As she walked to the waiting car, Little May said, 'What shall we call him?'

'Fortunato!' called Mrs Frampton, without thinking.

'Good . . . a good name!' said Little May.

Well! thought Mrs Frampton, as the car bowled silently along the narrow, shaded road.

Who would have thought it!

HE was in a foul temper all week.

'I keep telling you,' she said, 'we have to adjust.'

But he grumbled, about the water being turned off, about the staff bringing in hordes of friends, non-residents who hogged the pool, though he never put a toe in the water himself, nor was ever likely to. He was sulky when she mentioned the sailing club, something was obviously wrong there.

I daresay he's not getting enough attention.

He was used to being the boss, the governor. Now he had become just another retired businessman, and a small one at that, by Euro standards. A small fish. In a much larger pond.

She looked at him covertly as he sat reading the *Daily Express* on the patio, his stupid yachting cap keeping the sun from burning his bald head.

Poor old beggar, she thought. What's he doing here? He's not happy.

But he hadn't been happy at home. He had never been a man for friends or relations, always suspicious of being done. During the last years the business had ceased to expand. He had had to paddle harder to stay in the same place, they'd been lucky to get out as well as they had. At least he was warm here. No more catarrh, bronchitis, not even a cold all winter. And with a bit of luck her friend Phyl, who'd buried two husbands and always chivvied him up with a bit of flattery, would be down soon. Yes, just get through the next month, and look forward to visitors.

'Anything you want? I'm just popping out to the library.'

They agreed to meet at the golf club for lunch. HE grumbled, but it saved washing up, and she knew he enjoyed the company and ordering the waiters about. To cheer herself up she changed into her blue checked dress with the pleats. There were some snobby women at the golf club. No need to look like the cleaning lady.

When she arrived, panting up the hill to the clubhouse with her four library books, he was deep in conversation with a group on the grass. She waved at him and got herself an orange juice and joined them. Most of the faces she knew. The tall man from the oil industry and his wife were sounding off to the Dutchman with the big stomach about the shortage of trained gardeners. Soon, as usual, the talk turned to property and prices, bargains, urbanisations, resales and investment opportunities. Mrs Frampton, finding nothing to say, said nothing. She watched a flight of birds twittering in and out of the wild lavender. What were they after, insects?

The men's laughter honked and bellowed and there was a sudden move to the patio bar for food. Mrs Frampton was left with Cynthia, the oilman's wife, Eliette, the Frenchwoman, a Swedish woman with an unpronounceable name, and Deborah and Priscilla, two Irish women who were sucking up to Mrs Oil. Talk turned to the Saint-Laurent shop in Marbella, to

the new nail clinic, to schools for Deborah's girls – her
husband was breeding horses for the Arabs, and the need to
book caterers early. Mrs Frampton, slightly apart in the chair
by the shrubbery, began to grind her teeth.

Now come on, she thought. You're getting as grumpy as
him. There's nothing wrong with any of them, they're not
wicked or anything.

But, listening and ignored, she heard the jostling for
precedence. And would have risen and walked off and
overfilled her plate with seafood if Mrs Oil, out of *noblesse
oblige*, had not turned to her graciously.

'Would you care to come, Mrs ah . . . '

'Sorry?' said Mrs Frampton, blinking.

'To lunch on Monday. We need volunteers for the
committee.'

'I'd be glad to help,' said Mrs Frampton civilly. 'I can't do
Monday, though, I'm having lunch with May Liu.'

She was greeted with a sudden, total silence. Even the birds
seemed to stop chattering.

'Madame Liu?' Eliette, the Frenchwoman, had eyes like
satellite discs.

'You mean Madame Liu?'

'Yes.'

'You know her?'

'Oh yes.'

'You have been to Casa Peking . . . I mean, the Casa
Morisca?'

'Yes.'

'We've seen her, of course, at the Marbella Club . . . '

'What's it like?'

'Do you think you could ask her . . . '

For the whole of lunch she was surrounded.

On the way back in the car HE said, 'What's all this about you
knowing Madame Liu? What have you been on about?'

'I do know her.'

'Shooting your mouth off at the club, making a fool of me.
There are a lot of important people there.'

'I do know her.'

'Like heck.'

But in the evening the telephone rang, and it was Mr Oil. Would he like to join a golfing party to Los Monteros? As she rolled heavily into bed beside him and picked up her Molly Keane, waiting for his snoring to begin, she thought Well, much good may it do them that I know May Liu. They can scratch their asses, they won't get inside that gate. But I have, and I will again. And she's a good woman. She may be worth millions, but she's decent. Those dogs are well cared for and loved. She's all right. Unlike them.

She found her place and began to read and was soon laughing in descant to his sonorities.

Chapter 9

THE UNLIKELY FRIENDSHIP between Big May and Little May prospered. The stout ex-nurse, wife of a retired businessman from Bradford, and the lady from Hong Kong, widow and mother to tycoons, meeting at first to inspect the progress of the dog they had rescued, soon found such pleasure in each other's company that they became frequent companions. Over silver trays in Little May's beautiful, silent house, over coffee cups in the old town in Marbella, over *tapas*, over fresh, grilled fish in the beach bars, they exchanged the stories of their lives. She the granddaughter of a Kwuo-min-Tang government official, reared in Swiss finishing schools, familiar with Ascot, Chantilly, the opera houses of the world, on first-name terms with the owners of masterpieces never seen by the public eye. A shy woman in her fifties, refined and slender with a perfect skin and an almost frighteningly reticent smile. And Big May, heavy-hipped and short-legged, round-faced with a North Country accent, reared on the farm with little formal education and trapped in a marriage of unremitting dreariness. A lover of painting and a natural if infrequent painter herself with an ability to sketch likeness and a dashing sense of colour. Both women with a son and daughter, worshipping their children and fearfully grateful to fortune for their healthy survival. Both hating pretension and selfish ambition but resentful of attention given to the vulgar and importunate. Both given to tears, to moods of depression, suffering too easily the pain of others, averting their eyes daily from the hurts and humiliations of the world. Both loving beauty, both lustful, greedy and passionate in their dreams.

People who saw them, heads together over the luncheon table, were baffled.

'What on earth does Madame Liu see in that dreadful Brit?

Have you heard her speak? Look at them, they look ridiculous!' But the relationship survived ridicule. Madame Liu's sense of humour was tickled by Mrs Frampton's direct perceptions. She savoured her uncompromising attitudes to class and hierarchy.

'Listen,' growled Big May, as they sat together at a charity fashion show surrounded by the rich and titled, 'when you've blanket-bathed as many as I have . . . ' and Little May had inclined her head ever so slightly towards a fearsome Spanish duchess who was picking her nose, albeit in a refined manner. The Mays had begun to laugh behind their massive programmes, and then collapsed helplessly as a gaunt giant of a girl came prancing onto the catwalk, entirely invisible behind a puzzle of maroon ruffles. They had escaped and sat on the grass, stuffing scarves into their mouths to hide the squeals; and gone into a café for cream cakes until, queasy, Little May had suggested a sauna and massage. Which would have been fine if Big May had not come over faint in the sauna. She was driven home in the dark blue Rolls, too mouldy to enjoy the sight of the Frenchwomen's faces as she was helped across to Numero Uno, Calle Favoridad. Little May had leaned out, her face blanker than usual with concern.

'You will be well?'

'Oh yes, I'm all right. Too many cakes.'

'Then, we will have our picnic?'

'Oh yes!'

HE was away on a fishing trip. The Mays had talked of a picnic for weeks. Both were saddened by the absence of birds, and by the generally held opinion that all the small birds were being trapped locally for eating. Reading indicated that a trip into the hills might provide some sightings, so, on the Sunday after Mrs Frampton's débâcle in the sauna, they set off in an open-topped Mercedes. Little May had provided the savouries, the salads and the drinks, and Big May the fruit and the puddings . . . she had pored for days over cookery books. Little May's appetite belied her fragile appearance, so Mrs Frampton had made lemon meringue baskets, chocolate almond cups, a small blackcurrant bavarois and, to be on the safe side, a strawberry angel cake . . . enough for a dozen, but you never knew – and there was Honoré the chaffeur who was French and would be sure to notice the food.

The day was idyllic, with a soft breeze. The honey smell of cistus and the heavy scent of the billowing pines was strong as they snaked up the minor roads at a steady pace.

'I'm hungry,' said Little May after an hour, and Honoré drew off the road and down a track and pulled onto a grassy verge under a large locust tree.

'Let's find a spot,' and Little May set off. Mrs Frampton put on her sun hat, followed by Honoré with the baskets and the rug. There was a sound of goat bells and soon the goats swirled past them on the narrow path, low-uddered, inky-brown and beige with their mild, slightly mad eyes. The young shepherd, shy and startled like his charges, waved his cap cordially.

'Listen,' said Little May. There was the sound of water. They descended to a small noisy stream, and drank white wine and ate almond biscuits with their feet in the water. And walked on, to earn their lunch, with Honoré muttering in the rear.

'Look, eagles!'

They stood and watched the eagles rising on thermals, high in the air, for a long time.

'What's that over there?'

Ahead, through the sparse trees, was a sheet of blue. What was it, a painted wall, agricultural plastic? They walked up a rise. And came upon wild irises as far as you could see. From the pines on the east to the curved sweep of olive trees on the right a bowl of azure soared up and met the paler blue of the sky.

The two women stood for a long time. It seemed sacrilegious to eat and drink but eventually the hampers were opened. Afterwards Mrs Frampton lay back against a bank, eyes closed, listening to the twitterings and occasional trills of invisible birds. She sighed. Who could believe that you could feel so happy without being young and beautiful. She had found a friend. A friend who not only didn't drain you, demand your time, your sympathy, but a friend who asked only to give, to enjoy your company. Without bossing, or needing you as a courtier. And without wanting to be given direction or stimulus, unlike so many women who seemed content to regard themselves as observers. Or worse still, as princesses, sitting in a dream of longing waiting for the magic to happen, for adventure and ecstasy to begin. For provision, by somebody else, to be made.

No, Little May is what friendship is all about. A pity she can't be patented, mused Mrs Frampton with a brief glance towards the neat head under the pale sunhat. Most people haven't the foggiest and she knows it all, without thinking. She smiled, thinking of Little May's reticence, her quick perception, her generosity held in firm bands of sense, her strong dislikes, her little vanities, her superstitions.

I don't think I've ever been so close to anybody . . . well, apart from the children, and that's different.

There was no doubt about it. The last few months had changed her life. There was something to look forward to, if not every day, then every week. And it wasn't to do with May's money, in spite of the lovely cars and the delicious meals in Romano's swanky new restaurant. It was to do with a liveliness that infected them both when they were together, not exactly a feeling of irresponsibility, though something close to it. Anything was possible. Little May travelled, and played her part in the social swim. But she was lonely.

And I was lonely. And now we aren't.

They had even begun to create a little circle of their own . . . Monsieur de Réchatin, who was cataloguing Little May's library, Señora Ruiz of the Chamber Music Trust, Señor García from the pueblo who worked for the government on hydroponics and who was a passionate Green and music lover, Sheikha Malika, the Arab lady with the progressive, indignant daughters. And Swedish Gudrun, the reasonable one with her pale, northern eyes.

We're becoming quite a set. Who would have thought it?

She felt a pang of conscience. But it was no good. HE didn't fit in. The one time he'd come to collect her from the Casa Morisca he had been struck dumb by the house, the gardens, the servants. There had been silence all the way home and his manner to her had been distinctly odd for days, almost greasy.

It had worn off soon enough, but after that she made her own way to May's and he seemed content to bathe in the glory of his wife's grand acquaintance and showed off constantly in the club, to her embarrassment.

'There is a house!'

Little May's voice, with its singing quality, made her sit up. May was standing on a rock, and pointing. Below them was a large house, almost hidden in the pines and the locust trees.

'Shall we go and see?'

They scrambled down the bank and joined a well-beaten path. The asphodels were out already, and acanthus leaves, dark and intense, glistened in the shade of the banks. They turned a corner.

And got the shock of their lives.

A huge man, with an enormous, hideous face, sprang out at them, howling and slobbering and making Little May scream.

'It's all right, May,' said Mrs Frampton, 'we've frightened him.'

She stepped forward and smiled.

'*Buenas tardes.*'

The huge fellow backed away, his eyes crossing in an attempt to discern her, and then loped off down the path with a weird gait.

'Come on,' said Mrs Frampton.

Around another corner was an open drive, flanked by old iron gates with curlicues and flower shapes, the grass growing through the loops and whorls. As they approached the house there was a smell of pigs. Past outhouses and stables was an open courtyard and a large oak door, ajar. Little May reached up and rang the bell and a young nun came out, wiping her hands.

'May we come in?' asked Little May. 'We are on a picnic. What is this establishment, please?'

'You are welcome. We are a home for those who need a home.'

They followed the young nun into a central courtyard where an older nun received them, lifting her head at the sound of the car.

'It is my chauffeur. He has come to take us away.'

'But please – would you like to meet our family? You are very welcome.'

Most of the residents were mentally handicapped, with brain-damage or Down's syndrome. They had their own chapel and their own pool, tapped from a lake. They grew their own food. The grass in the little valley grew green and sweet, chickens roamed free, and the rows of vegetables and fruit were orderly and cared for. They were offered cool drinks and Little May sent Honoré for the picnic baskets, which were shared with shouts of joy by the residents. Little May walked off with the Mother Superior, a short, swarthy woman with intelligent eyes. They stood across the courtyard, their heads together until Mrs Frampton, enjoying a gossip with one of the nursing nuns, was surprised to hear a small hiss followed by a shriek from Little May.

She said, without turning her head, 'What is it?' And caught the dark eye of the Mother Superior.

'This house and all the ground is to be taken away, is to be sold.'

Mrs Frampton crossed to join them.

'Yes,' said the Mother Superior. 'Now that the new reservoir is finished the whole valley will be developed for urbanisation.'

'But where will you go?'

The dark woman's face was tired. She smiled patiently but the submission on her face was not total and, as if aware of resistance within, she pressed her lips together, looked at them both and murmured, 'God will provide.'

'They sell their hay and fruit and vegetables in the villages below. And honey. They are self-supporting and want to expand. They want to build another house and have more people.'

'That's not going to stop the developers, though, is it?' said Mrs Frampton. Little May looked at her without expression.

They left, with handshakes from the nuns, with gifts of flowers and honey, and kisses and cuddles from the residents including the huge, hideous boy who waved from the gate until they were out of sight.

'It's enough to make your piles bleed,' said Mrs Frampton, ' . . . sorry, pardon my French.' Honoré, in the driving seat, looked round slightly at the reference to his nationality and Little May giggled.

'Solly?'

She *does* sometimes use Ls for Rs, thought Mrs Frampton. They drove home in silence.

That week Mrs Frampton had an excitement followed by a deep disappointment. Her son Michael, who had gone to Australia to work on in-vitro fertilisation, was being offered a post in the UK. He would fly to London and make a detour to Spain on his return. For three days Mrs Frampton sang aloud. And then came the second call. He had decided to stay with his present research for another year. The team had reached a plateau. The number of women being successfully impregnated was still low. There was the chance of a breakthrough. Yes, she had said, of course he must stay with it. From her own work on the wards she knew that the pain of the infertile couple was singularly piercing. Lacking the tragedy of positive loss or accident, there was a denial of life, a meanness that destroyed hope and happiness.

'You stay with it, love,' she had shouted over the hissing and whistling of the line to Melbourne. But afterwards she sat by the telephone for an hour, to be near Michael, and when HE'd come in demanding supper she told him to go and boil his head with such ferocity that he closed the door and sloped off to the club without a sound.

'I don't mind . . . I don't mind at all,' sobbed Mrs Frampton to Little May. 'It would be selfish. Just the same . . . '

The next day Little May sent round a rose tree, Madame Alfred Carrière, a beautiful Edwardian climber with fuddled pale blossoms that Mrs Frampton had been seeking in vain. But when she rang to offer thanks, Little May was unavailable. And the next day, and the day after that.

I wonder what I've done, thought Mrs Frampton. I haven't offended her, surely? The butler would have given her my thank you note. She rang again. And was told that Madame Liu was out.

It was hard to bear, the thought that for whatever unexplained reason, her friend was upset with her . . . or even worse, that she had suddenly tired of the friendship. Surely not? But she *was* a rich woman. Who was it said that the rich were different from us? Mrs Frampton, after four days, stopped ringing the Casa Morisca. She tried to keep busy but found she was listening for the telephone. She would come in from the garden, sure that she'd heard a ring. And the blessed thing would be sitting there, silent as ever.

Late on the Saturday afternoon she was having a rest on the *chaise-longue* when the garden gate bell rang. She heard him grumble and called out, 'I'll get it,' and got to her feet, hot and flustered. It would be the laundry, late as usual. But when she opened the gate, there was Little May, smiling, with Honoré, almost invisible behind a huge bunch of Easter lilies.

'Quick, May . . . ' said Little May, 'I need a large cup of your weak Darjeeling tea.'

'With a slice of lime?'

'And wild honey, please, if you have some left.'

And Little May walked straight into Mrs Frampton's lounge and put her feet up, just like an old friend, while Mrs Frampton poured Honoré a cold beer.

'What is it, what's up?' For now she could feel the excitement.

'I have brought you a present.'

'They're lovely!' said Mrs Frampton, sniffing the lilies with pleasure.

'No, no. I am glad you like them . . . no, no, no!'

Mrs Frampton, seeing that her friend was going to be maddening, made the tea. Honoré carried the tray out to the terrace table.

'How nice it is here,' said Little May as they sipped. 'You make a nice home, May.'

'So do you. In a way, it's harder for you.'

'Yes. We are clever, are we not?'

'Yes, and are you going to tell me, or aren't you?'

'I have bought a hill. And a valley – and I think, half a mountain.'

'Three quarters, Madame,' called Honoré, who some said

was the lover and who, being French, was no fool. Little May pulled a face at him.

'We are the trustees, you and I. We safeguard the house and the farm, for the nuns and the people there.'

Mrs Frampton looked away. To hide her tears.

'I did it for you. To make up for your disappointment for not seeing your lovely and handsome son. You are stuck with Antonio.' Antonio was the hideous boy who had frightened them. 'He must be your chevalier servant for now . . . for a little while.' Little May started to laugh and Mrs Frampton threw a ginger biscuit at her.

Chapter 10

'YOU SHOULD GO there,' called Eliette, the tallest of the three Frenchwomen. Mrs Frampton did a doubletake.

'Me?'

She was sitting at the next table.

'*Pourquoi pas*, it's very good . . . excellent for value . . . not expensive, not at all.'

They'd been on about it for half an hour. Mrs Frampton had seen the Frenchies waving their arms about but, tired from a trip to the market, she had collapsed gratefully on one of the punitive plastic chairs by the pueblo pool.

There was no doubt about it, the lanky Eliette *was* flatter around the middle. Her silk suit looked a treat with its narrow belt.

'What's the point? I'm not going to end up looking like you,' laughed Mrs Frampton.

'Leesten!' This was Simonette, of the speckled henna rinse. 'When my oosbahn daysair me I come to maximum weight eighty kilos . . . impossible – orreeble!'

Mrs Frampton did a quick sum and looked in her lap. That was near enough her own weight as of this morning on the bathroom scales. Fourteen stone, seven.

'*Is* it expensive?'

She noted with glee the Frenchwomen's response to the mention of money. They leaned forward, all talking at once, and waved a brochure at her. On the front was a picture of a slim, glamorous girl.

'Not for the likes of me, I'm afraid.'

'No, no, no, no, no!' That was Number Three, the hysterical Henriette. She was, as usual, waved down, this time by Henna Rinse.

'For every woman, old, young . . . recuperate after inter-

71

vention . . . for stress . . . after facial surgery,' and she patted her own jowls proudly. She had just had them tightened and, instead of her habitual expression of a disappointed bridesmaid after the throwing of the bouquet, now looked owlishly pleasant all the time.

'Can't afford it,' said Mrs Frampton, giving away points in the hope that they would leave off.

'It is important for the health. You are a nurse – you know. To have *grasse* is bad for this,' pronounced the lofty Eliette, clapping a claw across her non-existent chest to indicate her heart.

I'll believe you, thought Mrs Frampton at a tangent. But she took the brochure and put it among the cherries and peaches in her basket.

HE was out, playing golf. She made an egg salad, laid the table and then walked round the garden. The pink climber was still throwing flowers, even if they did clash with the Crimson Glory buds. Funny getting roses so early in the year. She leaned to smell a red rosebud and suddenly saw a small tendril.

Don't tell me!

Like a fool she'd planted a honeysuckle which had colonised the garden and strangled everything in sight within months. She removed the surviving remain. What a struggle it had been to get that honeysuckle out. She remembered the day all too clearly. She had come over queer from the pulling and heaving and felt funny for the rest of the day.

I used to garden all day long. Now I can't even bend if I've just eaten something.

She went inside thoughtfully and, resisting the temptation to make another Nescafé, picked up the brochure.

Trust the French to find a bargain. The prices were modest compared to Monsieur Val's salon where she went for her shampoo and sets.

I suppose because they're new they're touting for clients.

She did a few sums. Eliette was right. Signing for two days a week would be the best value. As well as exercise and massage you got free use of the sauna, and there was a separate beauty salon, and a health bar.

I'd never have the nerve.

The idea, nonetheless, stayed in her mind. On the Monday, trudging up to the market for fresh vegetables, she saw the place across the road.

It's that place.

And, after buying wild asparagus and broad beans and little lemons, and a red car for Manolo next door, she crossed over, waiting for ages for the policeman with his frantic whistle until her head began to beat in the heat. It was a relief to find that the woman behind the desk was English.

'I was recommended by Madame Armand.'

At the name, the Englishwoman caught her eye and they both grinned.

'Aye,' said Mrs Frampton, 'she never leaves off, does she? We're neighbours.'

'I'll tell you something,' said the other woman, 'she knows what she wants.'

'She does that,' said Mrs Frampton. And before she knew it was sitting in a nice chintzy room with a cup of lemon tea.

'No biscuit, you notice,' said the lady, who announced herself as Sylvia Sanders.

'How did you guess?' sighed Mrs Frampton.

They had a look round together and Mrs Frampton was daunted. 'Don't be put off because they all look younger. This is group rate day, it's much cheaper, so the young ones are here. Come and meet Doctor Guttman.'

Doctor Guttman turned out to be an elderly Spanish woman with a moustache. Her English was excellent and she drew you out. On learning that Mrs Frampton was a nurse she offered her a job on the spot. Mrs Frampton smiled and said she'd given it all up years ago.

'Well, first things first. Time enough, yes, Sylvia?'

'That's how I got roped in,' said Sylvia Sanders, laughing. 'I came for treatment and I've never worked so hard in my life!'

They weighed her and took her blood pressure. Doctor Guttman asked questions. Measurements were taken. They showed her the swimming pool. As a girl Mrs Frampton had been a strong swimmer, having strong shoulders. She had won prizes but it was years now since she had owned a costume.

The pool was enormous and, like all of them on the coast, luxurious by British standards. It was cut ingeniously into the side of the hill behind the new building, with a long verandah above with chairs and tables and huge rubber trees giving privacy and shade. Several elderly women were in the pool, one on a ring, paddling gently with her eyes closed, one doing exercises in a corner with a young girl in a white coat kneeling at the edge.

'Only ladies,' said Doctor Guttman. 'We don't mix. Here is not for sex. Here is for work. And contemplation.'

'All right,' said Mrs Frampton with a sudden blush. 'I'll do it.'

'Good,' said Doctor Guttman, 'you are wise. Not a day too soon, if I may be open. Weight is never good and you are a nurse, a useful person – if you change your mind we are short here.' Which made Mrs Frampton laugh since the doctor stood six feet in her socks.

Gay too, I reckon, thought Mrs Frampton. Probably got some fluffy little woman friend, she looks the traditional type.

She didn't know how to break it to him. There was the question of the money.

There's nothing for it but to go straight in, she told herself, so she did, as soon as he had finished his dinner.

'You did what?'

'I've been feeling twinges. Round my heart.'

'See a doctor, then.'

'The woman there *is* a doctor. She recommends I take the course.'

'Well, she would, wouldn't she?'

But, surprisingly, he made little fuss. Nothing like the rows that would have rumbled on a year ago. Perhaps, after all, the sun and the fresh air, the lighter diet, the walks in the hills were having an effect despite his critical moanings. Later, he said he'd done well on the links. So that was it. At all events, on the Tuesday she went for her first treatment and paid over the cheque.

There, now I shall have to do it.

The going was not easy. By the third week Mrs Frampton was fedup. She had stuck to the diet but little weight was coming off and she was getting disbelieving looks from Marie-Angeles, who was in charge of her progress. The sauna made her feel dizzy and she felt a fool in the classes and couldn't do most of the exercises. The only one who kept her going was Frau Hauptmann, by being even fatter. They panted together and were miserable. But the exercises she did at home gave her pleasure. She could pace herself. She swung her arms and legs and hips and tried the running on the spot, though this made her pant and feel sick at first. By the end of a month she had lost six pounds and been given a red rose by Doctor Guttman for effort.

She did it. At first her face looked saggy, and she still felt hungry in the night. But the coming of summer made it easier. You didn't feel hungry in the heat. She found she wasn't panting going upstairs and even ran for the bus one hot Wednesday morning, alarming herself. But there was none of the expected pounding in the head, no black spots before the eyes. One day, accepting a piece of chocolate from Señor García's little granddaughter, she found it unbearably sweet after the months of dieting. That was a breakthrough, and she bought herself a new blouse the same day, an Emmanuelle Khanh in beige crêpe with self-embroidery in a twenties style. It made her look low in the bosom so she bought a new bra. And found she was a size smaller. She and Gudrun celebrated with spritzers in the pueblo bar.

The Frenchwomen came back, one after the other, at the beginning of the autumn, awash with new clothes from Paris and avid for local gossip. They noticed Mrs Frampton's new dimensions immediately.

'Ahhhh!' said lofty Eliette, sucking in her breath. She stepped back and threw up her ringed claws, sending a passing waiter careering towards the pool.

'*Voilà! Bravo . . . bravo! Mais voilà* – Simonette, Henriette . . . *la voici!*'

'*Alors!* Congratulation!'

'*Oui, oui, oui, oui oui!*' And they all walked round Mrs Frampton in her new blouse and bra. Their admiration was genuine and prolonged and Mrs Frampton felt a prick of tears. To have impressed those harpies, the Ettes as she called them . . . who would have thought it?

They grilled her exhaustively. How much weight, how many treatments, what regime, what prices?

'We moss 'ave a celebration!' said Simonette, the divorcee, who liked parties.

'*Un* cocktail perhaps?'

'More than that.'

'*Oui, oui, oui, oui, oui!*' That was Daftie, Number Three.

They went on for ages, as usual, and in the end May found that she had been coerced into a do on her patio. Further discussion ensued and the tables became crowded. Should men be invited or should it be *solamente* ladies? Should the food be *minceur*, or should it cater for larger stomachs? What of wine? In the end Mrs Frampton, hungry for her light lunch, began to get ratty. It was clear who was going to foot the bill though Gudrun offered to bake apple cake before being shot down and two Scotswomen, fearing a shortage of whisky, promised to bring a dram.

If it's my do it's going to be my way, she thought and, surprising herself, rose to her feet and shouted above the noise.

'All right, everybody, simmer down. It's my shout, so leave it all to me. Friday week, nine o'clock. I shall be sending invitations.'

'*Oui, mais . . .*'

But Mrs Frampton was halfway across the terrace. If I'm paying, I'm choosing, she thought grimly.

The mood of determination soon vanished. Mrs Frampton had stayed clear of the competitive entertaining that dominated the coast. While most of the husbands played golf and drank, the women gardened and embroidered, gossiped and entertained. With husbands retired and children grown they felt released, even skittish. They blessed their luck to be out of cold and ugly northern towns, away from strikes and political unrest, if not terrorism itself. They wrote cheques for charity, read romances and watched situation comedies on Gibraltar television. If nameless fears crept up through the sewers, if feelings of deprivation, of misuse, of something precious wasted infected conversation, then those feelings were quickly and firmly smothered. What was there to get upset about? They were happy. Or they would be, except for all the violence in the world. And all the hungry children – that had to be put right. And yes, it would be nice if their own children visited more often. Mrs Frampton missed her children. But she valued their freedom more and was puzzled by the anxieties around her. Even Little May seemed oppressed, although of course she was rich. It carried burdens.

Funny, I never feel worried like so many of them, she thought, weeding the marigolds. It makes you feel left out, in a way. She stood up, grunting, and suppressed old nightmare feelings of not belonging, of being unacceptable. And smiled to herself.

Never mind worried, I feel rage all right. Plenty of that.

She thought Now, now, don't wreck the day by going into one of your mean moods. You've got a party to plan.

She walked up the garden path.

By gaw, I'd like to knock their eyes out, and she started to laugh.

You cow! You're no better than the rest of them!

In the end she went for advice to Little May who, pale and exhausted, had just returned from Hong Kong. She listened in her usual silent manner. And then laughed her little laugh.

'I know,' said Mrs Frampton, 'I'm going to get my pride dented. Let's face it, I was never a light-handed cook.'

'Lighter than you were,' said Little May wittily and they both collapsed in giggles until they wept.

'I doubt it'll lift my puff pastry!' shrieked Mrs Frampton.

They walked through the gardens and smelled the late lilies, getting pollen on their noses, and stood admiring the sun on the feathers of the male peacock. By the lily pond Little May said suddenly, 'You must show off.'

'How?'

Little May grimaced as a peacock let out an unbearable shriek, then turned with a smile and patted Mrs Frampton on the arm.

There was still the matter of toilette. What a fool she had been to wear her Emmanuelle Khanh to keep her end up when they all came back from Paris. Now she would have to look for something else. She asked the big Dutchwoman and together they visited a new boutique in San Pedro but there was only a huge blue dress that made her look like a campsite.

At least it's too big!

But she was no further on after a morning in Marbella. She would have to go to noisy, tiring Málaga. She took a bus to the Puente Romano tennis courts where the Dutchwoman's younger daughter, the one with the pretty broken nose, was playing in a tournament. She sat for a while watching young Willa get beaten, and then fled to the shade of the cool, spacious bar. The Frenchwomen, canny as ever, were ahead of her.

'Where can I buy something to wear?' asked Mrs Frampton. 'I thought it would be easier, now I'm not so big.'

They gabbled in French and assessed her with narrowed eyes.

'You must go at once to Marcelline,' said Eliette, the tall one. 'You wish this for ther partee?'

'Oh, there's not time to have something made,' protested Mrs Frampton, but before she knew where she was they had whisked her in Henriette's daft little car into the old town in Marbella. And parked on the pavement.

Marcelline was fearsome. She was even thinner than Eliette, with a deep red line for a mouth and lifted everything. She walked round Mrs Frampton, said nothing, breathed close, then stepped back and pronounced in a grave and shocked manner, 'You 'ave vens.'

'Vens?'

Oh, she meant veins.

'You 'ave neglect your skeen.'

My skin? What's that got to do with it? thought Mrs Frampton, bewildered. There was a fusillade of rapid French all round and then out came a little Spanish woman with a tape measure and another with bales of cloth . . . blue slub, mauve angel-skin, artificial silk in tan with a faint grey overprint, green check silk, pink and brown silk stripe, swirls, zigzaggy yellows, lavenders, cornflower blues on a rose background; in the end Mrs Frampton was utterly confused. So many lovely materials, so many colours. First class, all of them. And undoubtedly expensive. She drew the lanky Eliette away from the bales with difficulty.

'Look, how much is all this going to cost me?'

'But I have explain, it will be *tout simple*, jus' a leetle dress and jacket, no pleat, all plain, jus' with lining. Important for you a good strong fabric.'

'I'll need to know how much,' said Mrs Frampton, her colour rising with embarrassment.

She thought she would pass out when they told her. She sat down, her mouth clamping together like the redoubtable Madame Marcelline above her. No. It wouldn't do. It wasn't on. Not that she couldn't afford it. There was enough money in the bank account. She could get him to write a cheque. Or use the Access card and give the old so-and-so a heart attack at the end of the month. Why not? Why not, for once in her life, have a decently made dress. There was no doubt about it, the Ettes always looked the thing. That was the trouble with them. They put you down by just coming into the room. But they were all thinner. Down to twelve stone from fourteen, Mrs Frampton thought dolefully to herself, I still won't look like them. Anyway, you need to be French. She felt a piece of pale silk fabric wistfully.

Never mind how much body it's got, it's still going to wrinkle on me. I shall still look like somebody's cook-housekeeper.

She wavered as they all chattered like machine guns and rifled through the bales. What had she got herself into? *And* they'd taken the trouble to drive her in. The swirls of French rose round her.

I bet they're asking for discounts for bringing in a new customer. Oh dear. She would have to go through with it. And not enjoy it. Oh, how silly.

She looked out of the window and across the road to the old man who sold cigarette papers. As she watched, he spat, and then got up. He was horribly crippled. Congenital, she thought, as he crawled, crablike, up the hill. There's so much to be done.

She turned away from the window and heard herself say, 'Look, this is going to take a while. I must go away and think.'

'But you 'ave no time!'

'I'll come again this evening – at six . . . all right?' And she smiled brightly.

They weren't fools. There were sharp looks all round but Madame Marcelline, with the smile of a Richelieu, kissed her on both cheeks and ostentatiously ordered the little woman with the bales to leave them out for further inspection.

'I won't come back,' said Mrs Frampton in the street, 'I've got some errands to do. Thanks ever so much, you've been ever so kind.'

Ruffled, they left, bumping into one of the hideous local rubbish bins. And Mrs Frampton went up to the big old Spanish drapers at the back of the town and bought a black rayon dress with a lowered waist and appliquéd satin sash, a style left over, she felt, from its design in the early thirties, to judge by the age of the shop assistants. She bought a real tortoiseshell comb, making the salesman's day, and a lace mantilla. And found some low black courts, not as stylish as the winkle pickers the women had worn in the Holy Week parade, but near enough. They were a size too big and comfortable, and the bit of a heel gave her height. Hot, and laden with parcels, she took a taxi home.

'What have you been up to?'

'Getting ready for next week,' she yelled, and dashed upstairs.

In her blue and white bedroom Mrs Frampton looked at herself in the cheval mirror they'd found in the *rastro*, the local antique market.

I don't look an ounce over ten stone, she thought, blessed if I can't see my cheekbones. The shoes lifted her up beautifully.

I look dignified.

She would wear a red rose in her bosom, and her seed pearl necklace from Michael. Funny, she would never dare go out like this at home, all dressed up and looking like someone else. Here it was different.

I look champion.

She put the dress reverently on a hanger, smiling to herself.

I'm looking forward to Friday.

With Little May providing the food, with three of her staff in attendance, and with Little May attending herself in diamonds and sea-blue silk voile, it looked as though the party might well be a night to remember.

Oooh Lord, she thought, I mustn't forget to ring that Madame Marcelline.

Chapter 11

YOU KNOW YOUR trouble, May, thought Mrs Frampton to herself as she hovered by the gate, you've lost your nerve. She followed the men up the garden path and instructed them in Spanish to leave the wine in the hall in the cool.

You're an old yellow belly.

How on earth had she been talked into this?

Me, entertaining? Wasn't she the one who sneered at other women in the pueblo who lamented a lopsided soufflé or a roux that hadn't rouxed?

It's never been my sort of thing!

Mrs Frampton, now in the last preparations for her party, dwelt briefly on those awful middle years back in Bradford, remembering hours of making conversation with ugly men whose only apparent virtue was a heavy politeness that she had always found vaguely insulting.

Still, I don't suppose I was any more attractive to them than they were to me.

Even worse had been the poor wives. It was hard now to recall a single face. The wives, to put it mildly, had lacked definition. Their terror of being a nuisance, their deference in doorways, necks and asses stuck out in apology, their diffidence over arrangements had tended to induce in Mrs Frampton regular waves of murderousness. There had been one famous occasion at a Rotary Club night out when a tiny woman in red crêpe, flushed with drink, had begun to laugh and to shriek insults during the Royal Toast. Her husband, grimly genial, had attempted to remove her, and there had been a terrible fight with the woman cursing and spitting in his face. In the ladies' cloakroom afterwards there had been a good deal of oohing and clucking, but it was still palpable in the memory, the *frisson* that had run among the other women at the sight of that daring and impossible act of rebellion.

Nearly eight o'clock. Mrs Frampton looked at herself in the glass in the downstairs hall. The mantilla had gone well in her robust curly hair which she had had rinsed back to its darkness for the occasion. Now, in the new black courts (worn in over the last week), a Crimson Glory rose at her waist, wearing her seed pearl necklace, an ivory bangle and several squirts of L'Air du Temps, there was nothing left to do but stand by the patio door with a churning stomach. What if the rest of the food failed to arrive? Could those crates possibly be enough to drink?

'Remember, the hostess is not there to enjoy herself, she is there to see to the enjoyment of her guests', the article in *Harpers* had said. Right. First show them where to leave their things, do their hair, go to the lav. Then see that everybody is introduced to several people. Keep looking to make sure nobody's stranded. Mix them up, don't leave one laughing group with everybody else left out, swish them round, haul them off to meet somebody else. Then . . . what was it? Keep the drinks moving. Top up glasses all the time, it looks generous and makes the drinks go further than if you let them sup up before you refill.

Oh heck! Cigarettes! She had remembered to polish the two silver boxes and then forgotten the damned cigarettes. Mrs Frampton rushed indoors and tore open the packets feverishly, breaking a nail – *and* she had paid for a manicure! Damn. And where to put the bloody things; whatever you did nowadays you were bound to offend somebody. Well, so long as they didn't set fire to anything – yes, that was it. She took the boxes outside and put one on the terrace and one on the garden table. That would save them from stinking up her lovely curtains. She regarded the violet-blue voile with the tiny Moorish pattern lifting in the breeze. There was no doubt about it, the house looked a treat. And, best of all, HE wouldn't be back from his fishing trip until after eleven. By then the party should be well under way, with drinks at nine and food at ten.

We should be buzzing, let's hope so, then he won't be able to come in and hump over everything.

She had laid out his things in the bedroom. With a bit of luck he'd be tired after a day on the boat. She would give him a stiff whisky as soon as he showed his face.

The bell rang. Mrs Frampton's stomach went.

'Oh Lord . . . Emiliana, could you?'

Emiliana from next door, invoked as neighbour-helper, bustled through from the kitchen. At the open garden gate stood Honoré, with the elderly Luis, Little May's major domo, resplendent in black and gold and white gloves, and Antonio and Juan, the footmen, looking like two Castilian princes of the blood. Behind them peeped Rocio, Little May's personal maid, armed with her box of combs and pins to be on hand in the bedroom. Mrs Frampton, her stomach failing her altogether at the sight of this awesome magnificence, dived for the downstairs lavatory which had been repaired for the umpteenth time to be pressed into no doubt temporary service. Honoré opened a bottle of Agualibra.

'*Courage, Madame.*'

Mrs Frampton could only manage a tiny smile. She stayed near the lavatory but felt better after the drink.

What the heck have I got myself into?

The Mexican Trio arrived.

By ten o'clock the party was purring along like a Bentley. Little May arrived and was received with awe by Lyn and her mother. She was escorted to the best seat in the garden where Simonette of the henna rinse, in surprising *décolletage*, made a weird obeisance, backing into Mrs Frampton's lilies.

'Why is she showing her chest like that?' whispered Mrs Frampton to her friend Gudrun.

'She wishes to be catching a man.'

'Oh dear.'

'Don't worry, she will.'

'Oh. Good, well that's all right, then.'

People arrived (in greater numbers by far than the list of invitees), were greeted and given drinks. They smiled and circulated and listened to the discreet rhythms of the Trio. The Garden Society ladies were welcomed and, in a graceful gesture, presented red roses to the ladies and gardenia buttonholes to the men. Mrs Frampton began to perspire and wonder if she should change her shoes. But decided against it. A feeling of floating, of being slightly above the ground, dispersed minor twinges. The party was going well! You could feel the happiness rising like champagne bubbles on the velvety night air. Unable to eat anything, she sidled along the white damask cloth of the buffet table, breathing pleasurably over the quails' eggs in their nests of moussed trout, the salmagundi, the pale whorls of Serrano ham, the towering castle of strawberries. If only she had thought to take a snap of it all before it started getting wrecked!

Luis García offered her a flute of champagne and she bore another to the local dentist, reeling slightly from his bad breath as he introduced her to his five (uninvited) children. Doctor Guttman from the beauty clinic arrived, resplendent in silver lamé, and her friend, who turned out to be a fiery little Catalonian, presented Mrs Frampton clairvoyantly with a book on the care of the feet. Three musical students, as arranged, arrived from Málaga to sing old Spanish songs and, as the harmonies rose, a dreaminess set in among the guests. Even the Frenchwomen piped down, only the chink of their bracelets betraying a steady rate of consumption.

The boys ended their recital with a song about one Esmeralda, who, it appeared, was wont to say no with the lips but yes with the eyes. The Spanish seemed to find this song unbearably provocative and applause was prolonged. But the star of the evening was undoubtedly the much loved international opera singer Gino Conti, who left his festive restaurant to come and sing Verdi and Puccini and Leoncavalli, and, after wild entreaties, 'Sorrento' and 'Amazing Grace', finishing gloriously with 'O Sole Mio', but to words of his own about an ice-cream, to screams of delight. After which the Mexican Trio broke into a spirited rumba and dancing began. Mrs Frampton had cleared her patio doubtfully but people crushed onto the space and jerked and wobbled happily in unselfconscious contortions. Reared on the quickstep and the foxtrot, she stood back. But was flattered to be steered round by Honoré, and then by her neighbour, Luis García. She pulled a silly face at him, laughing.

'I'm not much of a dancer, I'm afraid.'

But *he* was. A wiry little chap, he swung her about manfully, and then clutched her mournfully to his breast as the music switched to a tango, allowing Mrs Frampton to get her breath back.

'I must look after things.'

Mindful of her duties, she broke away to do her rounds. Little May was being wonderful. From the corner of her eye Mrs Frampton saw her, shining like a firefly, smiling and talking in her sing-song voice, drawing people to her with the brilliance of the shy when challenged to perform. She's a star, thought Mrs Frampton, gawping fondly. She watched Little May abstract young Lyn from her mother, include her in a conversation with the Countess and then steer the girl gently towards the student with the kind eyes.

There's nothing she can't do.

Turning away, she felt hungry for the first time of the day and scooped up Gudrun and young Remedios from next door. They sat together under the olive tree with plates full of salmon and lobster and exotic salads. And Mrs Frampton, maddened by Gudrun's second helping of summer pudding, allowed herself a small taste, but without the cream.

She was swilling down her pudding with champagne when there were loud squeals from the Frenchies. A contingent of late arrivals was coming through the garden gate. It was HIM, together with Gottfried from Calahonda, two other Jerries from the fishing party, an Irishman who was reputed to be the local cannabis supplier and a Mr Vaughan. Mrs Frampton, expansive with food and drink and feeling in her glory, drew them towards the drinks table, though she soon realised they had anticipated the moment since they all breathed whisky fumes over her genially. Gottfried, who had shown signs before when drunk, was particularly effusive and pushed Mrs Frampton up against the olive tree under the borrowed fairy lights.

'I haff oll day on the boat carried my smoking,' he boomed, indicating his dinner jacket.

'That was nice of you, Gottfried.'

'Not at oll. For you, I wish to make a solid good impression.'

'You do and all.'

He beamed and pressed so close that she asked after his wife who was having her piles removed in the Marbella clinic. Gottfried, however, was not in a conjugal frame of mind, and to offload him Mrs Frampton steered his majestic bulk towards the dance floor.

What must we look like, she thought, and – as he banged her hard into a young couple, toppling them onto the local priest – May the saints do you a bad turn for that, you horrible Kraut . . . However, he soon capered away with Beanpole and then with Daftie, who was very alive indeed with drink and who screeched incessantly like a factory siren.

It was time for the fireworks.

The fireworks had been laid on by Eddie from the beach bar. Together with his live-in partner, the achingly handsome Juan, he had set up his displays on the beach just beyond the garden wall. Miguel from next door, Gudrun and Mrs Frampton began to round up the guests and shepherd them onto the sands for the spectacle. It took some time to get people's attention and HE began to bellow bossily until she hissed at him to shut up and diverted his attention to the Ettes. Then Eddie let off a splendid rocket and soon everyone surged into the lane and the beach beyond. Eddie and Juan capered, black silhouettes, tapers in hand.

'Are you ready?'

Well! thought Mrs Frampton. If this isn't the best ever! She stood by Little May who clapped her hands like a little girl at the Catherine wheels, the shoots and the fountains, the pink and gold sprays and the dancing crackers. The first large display, in the shape of a dolphin, was set alight to murmurs of amazed delight, then the second, a depiction of the Concha, the beautiful mountain behind them, and then the third. And to May's delight, the third display, sparkling and crackling with fire, spelled out her name. Her eyes filled with tears and she turned to her friend. And Little May smiled and Mrs Frampton realised whose idea it had been.

The party was getting rowdy. Now that the big displays were

guttering, people began to claw at the smaller fireworks and the sparklers.

Oh blow! thought Mrs Frampton as a banger came whizzing through the air. Daftie, drunk as a newt, lurched about wildly, a firework in each hand.

'Come on, pack it in!'

But people were laughing and Daftie, encouraged, threw the fireworks over her head and grabbed two more, screaming with glee as they were lit. Mrs Frampton turned away to follow Little May up the path. But was arrested by sudden loud shouting. As she turned back a flame licked the air, followed by pungent smoke, as people came hurtling past her, shouting and screaming.

What on earth . . .

Gottfried's Mercedes had gone on fire.

It all happened so quickly that there seemed nothing to do (after the petrol tank exploded with an engulfing roar), but stand and watch. Daftie, vaguely troubled, took off, plunging away over the sands in high heeled shoes. Mrs Frampton grabbed her husband and gave him a push.

'Go after her, Vic, go on. The woman's a bloody menace, God knows where she'll end up.'

She watched him lumber off into the night and turned back to the leaping flames. People drew closer as Gottfried, with a glass of whisky, stood by stolidly, as close as the heat would allow, shaking his head slowly in imperial and drunken detachment.

'We won't forget this party in a hurry,' said young Lyn wistfully in the arms of Felipe the student, her mother, for once, nowhere in sight. That got a cheer and enthusiasts began to pile driftwood onto the glowing fire, and Beanpole, revealing a surprisingly unexploited talent, broke into a high nasal rendering of 'Non, Je Ne Regrette Rien'. Side by side the two Mays watched as, with supplies of fuel running out, the car burned away to a glowing metal frame. And Mrs Frampton, drawing closer in the cooling night air, was invaded by a mood of placid reflection.

I can't see all this happening in Bradford, she thought to

herself. Not even on a Saturday night. England seemed a long way away.

'Excuse me,' said Mr Vaughan in her ear, 'I don't want to bother you but I think the downstairs toilet is out of order.'

Chapter 12

'OH MIKE,' SAID Mrs Frampton, 'it's awful, honestly.'
They were sitting together in the tea lounge of her son's hotel in Bayswater. Called over to assist in the establishing of a new in-vitro department of a London hospital, in England for three months, he had been unable to make the journey to Spain. Mrs Frampton, with a great deal of difficulty, had squeezed the fare out of her husband, in the end by a sullen silence, and by serving fish, which he hated, every dinner time for a week. They exchanged reminiscences of HIS meanness . . . how he would charge the children fines for forgetting to wipe their feet or close the gate, how she had been enjoined to put sultanas or currants in a cake, not both, how the children had been forced to read with torches in bed after he'd turned off the light at the main in the evening.

'I don't know to this day how you passed your exams,' said Mrs Frampton fondly, gazing at her son. He seemed taller than ever, and even more like her brothers. His hair was fairer, from the Australian sun, his skin bronzed. 'You be careful,' she said, stroking his hand, 'don't get too much sun, you don't want to get skin cancer.'

'Oh, get off.'

'You sound quite Australian.'

It was odd being in England again. Everything looked so small . . . and so dirty. After the buoyancy of Spain, with its handsome King and young government, England seemed frowsty. The papers were full of local political rows, stand-offs, set-tos in the House of Commons. Everybody seemed to be on the turn somehow. A weekend back in Bradford had not been a success. Old friends seemed lacklustre, not all that thrilled to see her, and less than interested in her news.

'What's gone wrong with the place?' she asked her son.

'Perhaps it'll be better when the Common Market opens up, and we're all one trading area. Nothing seems to be a going concern any more.'

'I know what you mean.' He was having the greatest trouble setting up his clinical facilities, not only because the funding was inadequate, but because he was getting little co-operation . . . even his old professor seemed askance at his intrusion. The Australians were becoming the experts in assisting barren women to bear children.

'You wouldn't believe the petty jealousy.'

'What are you going to do?'

'The job I came to do.' One of the problems was that the existing clinic, already staffed, had proved a failure, partly through lack of funds, partly through inexpert techniques.

'If only you could get a bit of publicity . . . do something that hit the headlines,' said Mrs Frampton.

'Then I'd really be in the cart.'

'Well, yes, but it might help funding.' Mrs Frampton had been helping her rich and influential friend May Liu on charity committees. She was becoming proficient in ways of extorting funds from diffident pockets.

At the beginning of her second week in London, Mrs Frampton was reading her *Daily Mail*. On the fourth page was the story of a woman, a nurse like herself, who had saved half a dozen children in a London fire. There was a picture of her on a ledge with a child in her arms. Underneath was a smaller picture of the woman with her husband, a nice-looking young chap. And in the evening, watching television in her room while waiting for her son, Mrs Frampton saw the pictures again. The young woman's name was Flora Kershaw. Her husband had leukaemia. What is more, they had been trying for seven years to have a child of their own. Twice they had tried clinical help. Twice it had failed.

'Mike,' said Mrs Frampton, when he came in to take her to dinner, 'look at this.'

Over dinner he said, 'Mum, there's nothing I can do. The list is a mile long. She's failed to get pregnant twice, and she's over thirty.' There was always a problem with choosing women for an in-vitro inception. If you took younger women you had more chance of success, and success meant support for the department, for further research. But older women had less time to wait.

'She's news, Mike.'

'Mum, even if I could get her on the course the chances of her becoming pregnant are pretty well nil. Anyway, it looks as if she's enough trouble on her hands with an invalid husband.'

'I know how to get hold of her,' said Mrs Frampton, 'the name of the hospital is in the paper.'

He read the article silently.

'What's the matter?'

'No wonder she didn't make it if she was treated there.'

He was quiet for the rest of the meal. As they were eating their strawberries there was a whoop from across the room and Chloe was punching her brother in joy. She had made it. Mrs Frampton, her eyes full of sudden tears, clasped her lovely girl, saw that everything was well and sat down happily. Chloe was working in Scotland and the rendezvous had been doubtful. Now everything was perfect.

'Listen, Chloe . . . '

They went on at him until he said all right, he would do what he could. Mrs Frampton rang the hospital and eventually spoke to Flora Kershaw who was, to put it mildly, surprised. But, like all desperate women, she agreed to an appointment with Mike. Time was short, but just before her goodbyes at Heathrow, Mrs Frampton learned that her son was to stay on in London for an extra four months.

'I'll try and get down to Spain.'

'That's a promise.'

'I'll try, but don't forget, it's a small world. We'll see you in Oz yet.'

'And you'll do something for that nurse.'

'Come on, take it easy, I'm not a magician.'

Seeing the children unsettled her, and it took time to feel comfortable again. She framed her Polaroids and snaps and even HE looked at them when he thought she was out of the room. He asked after his daughter, as she had known he would.

And said not a word about his son. She told him anyway and he listened, smoking his pipe. She showed her pictures to Gudrun, who said that Michael reminded her of Robert Redford; and Henna Rinse, the heaviest of the three Frenchwomen, called Chloe chic, which was amazing. Mrs Frampton rang her rich friend Little May, but she was again in Hong Kong.

Never mind, she'll be here when Mike comes. I can show him off.

But he didn't arrive. She was washing a beetroot one morning when the telephone rang and the familiar voice said, 'Hullo, what are you up to?'

'Nothing, when are you coming?'

'I can't. I've got to go to Baltimore.'

They talked, and she was bright, but the disappointment was keen. She wanted to show him her house, her new life, and talk about Spain and the socialist government. And now he wasn't coming, he was going to America. She felt a sullen misery invading as he talked and although she tried to keep up, began to find nothing to say.

'I'll ring again before I leave London . . . '

'Yes, if you would.'

'Give the old bugger a punch on the jaw for me.'

'I will. Take care of yourself.'

'Sure . . . well, goodbye – oh, by the way, remember Flora, the nurse you – '

'Of course, I had a card from her last week – '

'Her levels are up . . . way up.'

'You don't mean – '

'I do.'

'How many did you – '

'We got three embryos and used all three.'

'That means she's got at least two.' It was normal to insert patients with more than one embryo, as this meant that at least one was more likely to take in the heightened hormonal environment.

'Yup, in fact, she may have three.'

'What makes you say that? You can't tell at this stage.'

'I know, but it's odd. The night before we knew how many

we had on the slide I had a snack with her and her husband. She told us both that she was going to have triplets.'

'Oh well. You never know.'

They said their farewells and Mrs Frampton went over to the desk to write a note to Flora Kershaw. He wasn't coming.

Thank heaven I made the effort and got to London, she thought. At least I saw them both.

She stamped the envelope and went for a walk round the garden, the letter in her pocket.

I'll pop over to the main desk.

Emilio, in the pueblo office, would get the letter off in the afternoon mail. She walked across the garden. Yes, both of her children well and happy. A boy and a girl. She had been lucky. But three for the price of one? She smiled and then paused for a second, gazing round vaguely. It was early days, far too soon to guarantee that the pregnancy would last.

Oh yes it will, she thought, that girl knew before those babies were even inside her. They were alive, on a dish, and they were her children. She'll have them, all right. Anyway, Mike didn't make mistakes.

She let herself in.

'May?'

'Only me!'

She wanted to tell him about the triplets, but it wouldn't be any good. He'd call her a fool. But when he said he was eating at the club with friends, after all her work making the Caesar salad and the lemon meringue, all she said was, 'You go, love. Enjoy yourself, why not?'

He gave her a funny look but pushed off without a word, and Mrs Frampton sat down to enjoy the salad alone.

I feel like sweet and sour pork, miserable at Mike's not coming, excited about Flora Kershaw.

She got up to get a tiny helping of the pudding. What was that awful smell? She sniffed. It was the terrible aftershave he had come back with one night from the club.

'Throw it away,' she had begged after a sniff, but not him.

I *must* tell him not to use so much of it . . . he'll put off those who *are* still talking to him.

She went to make herself a cup of Nescafé. Perhaps she would go to Australia. Why not? But where was the money to come from? I'll think about that tomorrow, she thought, and settled down to John Thaw on Gibraltar television.

Chapter 13

'NO THANKS!' SAID Mrs Frampton. The last time she'd been on the boat she'd vowed never again. He'd shouted incessantly, sworn at Alonso, bawled down the hatch for his food, clouted her with the boat hook (admittedly, accidentally), and shown her up when they were coming alongside. That was it. She'd made up her mind. Never again. But the set of his shoulders as he leaned over his stupid charts made her change her mind. Fair's fair, she thought, I've been gadding about leaving him all on his own with a tin of sardines and a banana. What with the do at the library and the grand opening of Gudrun's new shop she had been more out than in.

'Who did you think of inviting?'

He looked up, the old smug look back in place.

'The girls.'

'The girls? Who? What girls?'

'You know.'

'No, I don't know.'

'You know. The girls! Eliette and . . . ah, the other two.' She nearly fell over.

'And Gottfried and Helge, of course.'

Him? On speaking terms with the cheesy Frenchwomen? The three harpies who had given Mrs Frampton sour risings and heartburn from the day she'd ventured shyly towards a chair by the pool, only to have a nasal rasp ring out that the poolside seats were taken. The memory of her gabbled apology still inflamed – she'd as much right there as they had!

'I didn't know you knew them.' She banged the saucepans into their wooden slots.

'Steady on, you'll chip the enamel.'

She looked at him in surprise. When had he been interested in saucepans?

He folded his charts with maddening deliberation. All right, so he wasn't going to tell her. If he'd fallen for that lot he was welcome.

'Oh, I know the girls all right. We've had many a drink at the bar.'

'Have you?'

'I've been giving Elie a bit of advice about her portfolio.'

Elie? The girls? What was he getting up to behind her back? Portfolio, I'll give him portfolio, she thought, putting her feet up for a rest. She smoothed the mercerised cotton bedspread absently and began to giggle.

So, when the cat's away . . . I wonder which one he fancies, Beanpole, Henna Rinse or Daftie!

True, there *was* an acute local shortage of men. Those who did not die soon after retirement were soon done in with the cheap drink or in the fullness of time popped off before their wives. The coast was full of single women, widows and divorcees, whining or relieved, triumphant, sorrowing, on the make or off the hook. The competition for available males was implacable. Mrs Frampton found it all baffling but fascinating. And saved up local gossip for her rich, reclusive friend, Little May.

'You'll never guess who's made off with the plastics factory man! The woman who wears the see-through blouses . . . and she's seventy-two. Mind you, she *is* Hungarian.'

But this . . . well, what did it matter? He'd get nothing from the trap-mouthed French contingent. And as for them getting anything out of him, well, rock and a hard place. Mrs Frampton, nonetheless, sucked her teeth thoughtfully.

What can they be after . . . his money? Can't be for his hairline. Eliette, with her boutiques in Marbella and Val d'Isère did well enough, but the hennaed Simonette's husband had decamped after the divorce and she had only the residue of the sale of her parents' house. As for Henriette, who could tell what *her* circumstances were since she never made any sense at all.

Never mind all that, thought Mrs Frampton firmly, plumping up the pillow behind her neck. What am I going to feed them on on this jaunt? Repressing a desire to prepare hot fried chicken in a tamale sauce, Mrs Frampton took up the challenge of providing a repast for a day on the water. Knowing him, she reckoned they wouldn't be going far, and this proved to be the case. Alonso would bring the *Cecilia*, named for the wife of the last owner but two, to Puerto Banus and, with his son Luca, act as skipper and crew.

Thank the Lord for that.

Mrs Frampton did not normally take the Lord's name in vain but after the delivery of white ducks, a smart yellow sweater and a cap with scrambled egg she had begun to have worrying thoughts of Mr Toad.

Embarkation was midday on the Sunday. Passengers and crew would enjoy a leisurely lunch on board, en route for the elegant resort and marina at Sotogrande, where the Mullers would disembark for a table tennis tournament of much exclusivity . . . an Arab prince was reputed to be a finalist. The main party, after a trip ashore, would motor back to Puerto Banus, tea to be served en passage.

Oh blow, thought Mrs Frampton, when this itinerary was explained in massive detail, I can see where I shall be spending the day . . . in the galley.

But curiosity raised her energy. At home he had never had anything to do with entertainment that was not directly concerned with business. As for inviting out a bunch of women, even a year ago he would have reacted to the suggestion as a sign that she was going off her head.

I wonder, mused Mrs Frampton. What are those blessed Frenchies up to?

Sunday dawned, clear and hot as usual. By eleven-fifteen Mrs Frampton was on the quay sitting on a bollard while, scanning the horizon for the *Cecilia*, HE walked up and down and bumped into people. She went over the food in her mind. Cold lemon chicken, smoked salmon, green salad, cheese straws and melon, with baby croissants and petits fours for later, everything in icebags ready to be taken on board. By midday neither boat nor guests had arrived. At one-fifteen the French contingent erupted from Henriette's miniature car with hoarse shrieks and debauched beachbags, binoculars, wraps

and cream cakes, Evian, enough wine to sink Paris and
Henriette's Tibetan terrier, Giselle.

'Giselle . . . Giselle!'

Daftie tottered off among the yachts in white high heels.
Mrs Frampton, who hated all the spurious posturing of the
yachting world, felt nonetheless shown up and ashamed of the
woman.

There was a consultation. HE was despatched to telephone
for news and the invitees retired to the nearest bar. Mrs
Frampton, after a large Punt e Mes, began to recover her
amiability. What did it matter if the trip came off or not? A
picnic in the hills was a much better idea.

The Germans arrived, Gottfried like a war cartoon with thick
neck and his stomach carried before him. Mrs Frampton, safe
behind her mirrored sunglasses, viewed him with sexual
distaste. That men should *want* to look thus was baffling. As
for the wife, one look at that Easter Island profile and your
veins began to ache. She was all fixed points. She took
everything you said literally, and when her husband said
anything, she said it again.

'The car does not start. We are late.'

'We are late. The car is not starting.'

They carried large swimming towels, snorkelling gear, a
white plastic radio and two vast wicker hampers. And within a
minute had demolished all the olives and crisps and peanuts on
the bar as Mrs Frampton, seeing her husband approach
through the heat haze like Omar Sharif in Lawrence of Arabia,
averted her gaze.

Poor old devil, his first do and it's gone wrong.

But, just as they were all moving off for *langostas* at
Romano's there was a toot-toot-toot and a wave from Alonso as
he manoeuvred alongside. Soon, despite HIS bellowed orders
and the abattoir honks of the French, they were all seated in
the sailcloth chairs on the afterdeck. Mrs Frampton, the wind
lifting the brim of her hat, raised her face to the sun with
closed eyes.

I'll have a ten minute snooze and then pop below and get
lunch.

Which proved to be less than simple. He would get in her

way serving the drinks. She had never known so much fuss. Did Eliette want ice, where were the lemon slices and Gottfried's special beer glass, what did the daft one want? That alone took a good five minutes.

He'll explode, she thought joyously. But no. He bobbed back and forth with a silly smirk on his face, in his element with Gottfried calling him Skipper. At last he removed his large behind and she was able to concentrate on her trays. First the tasty bits and pieces, then the chicken and salads, now the napkins – white cloth, not paper, for a bit of show-off – cutlery, the chilled Evian water.

'You want help?'

'Are you wanting help?'

'No thanks. Shan't be long.'

But when she pushed open the doors with her first tray, there they all were getting their faces round huge bread rolls stuffed with German sausage and gigantic wedges of cheese.

Well, blow me.

She could have hurled her delicate trays into the ocean. But was somewhat placated as the French turned to a new wave of free victuals with screeching cries of joy. Napkins were allotted and Helge's gigantic pork pie pushed aside. Mrs Frampton took her seat. It looked lovely, elegant and a proper feast. And she was hungry. I'm going to enjoy this, she thought, bending towards the salmon.

It was not to be. Suddenly the sun, unbelievably, appeared to switch itself off. The boat rolled slowly, and back again, scattering the glasses. Alonso shouted at Luca who began to move about quickly, kicking Helge in the bosom. Mrs Frampton stood up. Where was the Concha, the beautiful friendly mountain that reared its benign bulk behind the coast? There was nothing but a dark metallic curtain a few yards away and getting closer every minute. A few large drops fell on her face as Alonso yelled and the boy put up the dodger. A second later the squall hit them and laid the boat on its side. All three Frenchwomen screamed and Mrs Frampton pushed them quickly into the saloon where Simonette, wearing espadrilles with high wedges, fell over and gashed her forehead. Mrs Frampton produced medication. A German curse erupted on deck and the dog came flying in and was sick on her shoes. Holding on grimly and trying to sluice off her feet Mrs Frampton thought Poor old beggar. It's rotten luck. And tried not to laugh.

She lurched on deck, almost blinded by the searing rain and deafened by the wind. The boat was chugging forward with a reassuring indomitability. But the waves! They were gigantic! Beanpole stuck her head out of the saloon just long enough for the wind to whip away her headscarf and wreck her hairdo, and disappeared with an indignant glare. Mrs Frampton, getting a whiff of sickness from below, took a deep breath and went to assist.

'I want to go back!'

'Take us in at once!'

Henriette seemed to be praying.

'It's only a squall,' said Mrs Frampton. 'It'll be over soon enough.'

'No!' groaned Simonette, 'don't let eet do that!' as the boat lurched, and then lurched again.

'I demand that you turn around. Take us ashore!'

Mrs Frampton looked the lanky one in the eye. My turn at last, she thought.

'We can't. We'd never make it against this wind. One of the engines has packed up.'

'What!'

'What is the mattair?'

'Are we sinking?'

'No, of course we aren't, you silly cow. Now take one of these, all of you – try and keep them down . . . better take two. Take these and lie down and go to sleep. You'll be fine.'

After a good deal of trouble she got them all tucked in, and went up on deck again. The Germans, hunched side by side like a chorus from the Nibelungenlied, were eating steadily.

'The sausage is good.'

'This is good sausage.'

The squall was over as swiftly as it came. All of a sudden the sun was shining, the sea moderating, the air sweet and windless. Alonso whistled through his teeth, HE took off his new yellow oilies and fisherman's hat, and Mrs Frampton made tea for the deck party. Daftie was the first to appear, tremulous and uncertain. HE made a big fuss with cushions and rugs, and soon she was joined by Henna Rinse, whose unforgiving expression was not helped by the over-large Bandaid Mrs Frampton had slapped on her forehead. Lastly, Beanpole herself, recoiffed, now *en bandeau*, in a baggy white sweater and white shorts. The journey proceeded without incident, though the atmosphere was now subdued, enlivened only by the clinking of glasses as restoratives were circled and recircled. Alonso, out of respect for the mood, throttled back, but at last Sotogrande hove into view.

'We shall hire a car to take us home,' said Lofty firmly.

HE tried to reassure. Cost was mentioned. The Frogs dithered. Oh well, thought Mrs Frampton, at least we're getting rid of the Jerrys. Who left after much jovial snap-taking and instructions that the cheeses, the second sausage, the pickled cabbage and the nuts were to be enjoyed in their absence, hampers to be returned pro tem.

'Enjoy the ping-pong,' called Mrs Frampton, awed by the sight of their splendid rumps. Gottfried turned with a severe expression.

'I hope that we shall win.'

'We are hoping we win.'

A solid good impression to the last.

HE took the 'girls' ashore while Mrs Frampton cleared up. She was minded to have a lie down on the foredeck, but the soft pluck-pluck of the water was almost too inviting. She hated falling asleep in the middle of the day. She always woke up irritable.

You need a walk, my girl.

She came upon the others as she passed a little shop selling beautiful and expensive jewellery. She had paused to look at a collar made of pieces of silver, flattened and slightly twisted, glowing softly on dark blue velvet. And then looked up to see them inside. The shop went on, through a corridor with showcases, to a little courtyard. She followed, unobserved. What *was* the matter with him? He was grinning and cocking his head like a daft old puppet . . . he even seemed to be affecting a nautical roll.

He's drunk, she thought, as she followed them into another, larger Aladdin's cave, the main shop. As she came up to them, in the cleverly lit gloom, her mouth dropped open. He was pronouncing loudly, not that he ever spoke softly, that the 'girls' were to choose a piece of jewellery each, a present from him to make up for the storm. She couldn't believe it! Was this the man who'd told her to dry out teabags, whose wedding present to his sister had been an EPNS jam spoon?

He *must* be drunk!

She tried to catch his eye, but, after a sour glance at the sight of her, he kept moving off like some great animal in a safari park when you were trying to get a snap. I wasn't supposed to be here, she thought grimly. She turned over pieces of jewellery, each more lovely than the last . . . a rose quartz and silver bracelet, fire opals, a smoky pearl choker with an amethyst clasp. A pair of silver ear-rings, simple and heavy, caught her eye.

I could wear those.

She looked at the price. Fifty thousand pesetas. Two hundred and fifty pounds? Crikey – had he gone bonkers? She picked up a snake necklace, pretending to display it for his admiration, and nudged him, pointing to the price. But he took no notice! Instead, he joined the prattling French who, egged on by the owner, were trying on like quick-change artists, grabbing with their red-nailed claws and dodging and diving like seagulls on the town tip. Mrs Frampton, defeated, took a seat.

At the end of forty minutes of drama, disagreement and indecision, Lofty chose a silver articulated belt with a topaz and lapis lazuli buckle, Henna Rinse a heavy bracelet dangling with silver rosebuds and Daftie, going the whole hog, snatched up a set comprising necklace, ear-rings and brooch in one of the few hideous designs on offer. Mrs Frampton sidled over as he took out his credit card but he turned his back so she couldn't read the amount. She picked up a little silver stick pin from the cheap tray on the counter and dug him in the ribs.

'I fancy this, Vic.'

'What do you want that for?'

She put it back.

Never mind. It was his day. But all that money! And to spend it on rubbish people. Mrs Frampton followed the merry party back to the boat. From the back, with his yellow top and white ducks, he looked like a poached egg.

I'm going to have to keep an eye on this.

But suddenly, despite her efforts at geniality, a blackness descended. The drink was wearing off, she told herself firmly. But the devil, having arrived, lodged himself firmly in her left ventricle.

'Hang on,' she called, 'I shan't be long.'

She hurried back to the shop and went inside. And picked up the necklace of silver pieces from the window and held it against her neck. Yes, it was as she'd thought. She had always had a good neck, white and soft. It was perfect.

'It is for you,' said the woman, coming up behind and looking in the glass over her shoulder. Mrs Frampton took the necklace off and glanced at the price. Two hundred pounds.

'I'll have it.'

The woman, alive with pleasure at yet another sale, looked her in the eye and smiled.

Yes, thought Mrs Frampton, you know what I'm up to. You saw it.

She walked back to the boat in a dream, the box with the necklace in her bag. In time to see the Frenchies climbing into a cab. She stopped, and watched him close the door after them and lean in the window chatting and giggling . . . he was giggling! And then give the driver a handful of notes. He was paying their fares! And it was miles back to San Pedro!

Never mind. The soft silver disks glowed in her bag, glowed on her neck, clinked softly in her heart. It might be sad, she thought, for a woman to have to buy her own jewellery. But at least you got what you wanted.

So did the Frenchies, said the devil in her heart. And spoilt it for her.

Chapter 14

FIRST HE WASN'T coming, then all of a sudden, after a week of sneering at her preparations, he was.

'What made you change your mind?'

He gave her a black look.

'Well, that dinner jacket will have to be cleaned, for a start.'

'It's not dirty.'

'No, but it smells of wardrobe.'

'Don't be so stupid.'

What did he want to come for? He didn't *like* the pictures. For years in Bradford Mrs Frampton had visited the local cinema by herself. It had kept her going through many a domestic crisis. She had been a witness to the rise of Sean Connery, who had turned those violent books into something good-humoured on the screen, right up to his profound and moving work in *The Name of the Rose*. She had read in an article that his sardonic edge in the film was from standing about in the cold in a habit and sandals, but that would have been just his joke. There was an impatience with rubbish about Sean. He was a decent man and it showed. And Michael Caine, with his funny eyes, who could play anything, and Alan Arkin, the American, though you didn't see him all that much. He'd been good in *Catch 22*, one of Mrs Frampton's favourite films. Like the book, it was true about the war. Pity that *MASH* had taken the limelight at the time, just because it was funny. *Catch 22* had been funny. But mad. Like the war.

Two films were to be shown at the charity première, *Jean de Florette* and its sequel, *Manon des Sources*. In French. Mrs Frampton's French was weak and reading sub-titles made her eyes tired, but the Blacks were running the evening in aid of local children and Mrs Frampton admired the Blacks. They were a glamorous older couple, he still a handsome devil and his wife Elizabeth, an ex-film star of the fifties, a joyously vivid woman of sparkling intelligence and totally without side. Both of them had an endearing sensibility and were generous, not only with their time and energy but with their pockets. And generosity was always a benison, an antidote, a reminder that life *did* exist out there, beyond the front door. So Mrs Frampton had coughed up a donation to Lizzie Black *and* managed to sell twenty tickets (including three to the Frenchwomen at a special rate which she had had to make up herself.)

There was the question of what to wear. Little May had indicated full evening rig and here Mrs Frampton was stumped. She had had a couple of long dresses but had shortened them long ago. She thought of approaching the Frenchies.

No, better not. They'll have me in over my ears before I can say ah!

In the end, after driving him mad with her indecision, she consulted Little May. Who gave her the address of a Spanish dressmaker.

'But there won't be time.' The première was a week away.

'Of course there will. Now, I shall be wearing beige-pink silk . . . ' They got down to specifics.

Emilia, the dressmaker, suggested a top in soft brown and blue angel-skin, with a skirt in alternate colours and a loose coolie over-jacket in darker blue with brown and pink, and wide self borders. To Mrs Frampton it sounded awful.

'Won't it be rather muddly?'

The bird-like Emilia smiled. 'Trust to me.'

Mrs Frampton, caught for time, felt she wasn't in a position to do anything else.

'I'll look a twerp, I suppose.' What did it matter? As the society beauty said to her daughter on her wedding day, who's going to be looking at you?

She would brave it out.

In the event, she was doubly surprised. When she went for the fitting – first the skirt, flaring out low, then the simple square top, then the loose-sleeved jacket –

'My word!' said Mrs Frampton. And turned and turned

before the long mirror. The clothes seemed to suggest a waist. She looked taller. And the colours! Her skin seemed softer, more alive. 'My word!'

The little woman was a genius. *And* her prices were low, so low that Mrs Frampton felt at once guilty and greedily excited. She could afford to do this again. *I wonder if I should get some streaks in my hair!*

She had his dinner jacket cleaned and on the night of the première cooked a supper of all his favourites, tomato soup, chump chops with roast potatoes, carrots and peas and a rum trifle with plenty of cherries.

That should put him to sleep in five minutes, then he won't groan and fidget and spoil it for me.

The première, in Spanish style, did not begin till ten o'clock at night. When they arrived, at nine-twenty, the huge space in front of the cinema was already crowded and noisy. A local band played Bizet's *Carmen* in deference to the French films. *I wonder,* thought Mrs Frampton, who knew that the opera offended many Spanish who thought it made them into stereotypes, and who complained that Bizet had stolen traditional airs. Camera bulbs flashed everywhere in the long foyer as Mrs Frampton thrust his ticket at him, told him to find two good aisle seats half-way down and dashed off to get her programmes and long-stemmed carnations, one to be given to every lady guest. Stewart Granger arrived looking brown and handsome and distinguished with his snowy white peak of hair. Royals and duchesses swirled through in lace and taffeta, lamé and tulle, in satin evening trousers, in glowing sequinned jackets. Princess Stephanie of Monaco arrived in a pink dress with no sides. *I suppose it's the fashion,* thought Mrs Frampton, attempting and failing to give her a carnation. The auditorium was filling up fast, with pushing and shoving for good seats. She noted with satisfaction that he was already *in situ*, his face glum because he couldn't smoke his pipe. She went down and gave him a programme, not daring to suggest that he might put his hand in his pocket for it.

'What time's this thing supposed to start?'

'Half past ten,' she lied.

'It's ten to eleven already.'

*

109

At half past eleven the Boys Brigade Band from Gibraltar arrived, gave a strong rendering of 'Scotland, the Brave' on the concourse and then proceeded round the aisles of the auditorium playing the bagpipes to whistles and wild applause. People surged out to the bars, back to the auditorium with large whiskies, out into the open where the photographers crouched and weaved and backed to snap Stephanie Audrun, stunning in black, and to let off a hundred bulbs at the arrival of Deborah Kerr in soft pink with a tulle wrap, and the Countess Bismarck, whose blonde hair, under the lamps, shone like the helmet of Brunhilde. The guest of honour, Danny Auteuil, star of the films, was driven up in a white Rolls with Isabel Adjani, who was making a film in Jerez. The excitement now began to spill over. So did the supplicants for seats. Little May, looking vulnerable in the crush, was thrown to Mrs Frampton's side.

'Too many people!'

The Mayor climbed genially onto the platform and announced that the films with Spanish sub-titles were to be shown in Salon Numero Dos. There was a concerted surge towards the doors and out into the foyer. The young ballet dancers who had been performing outside were swept aside like confetti. Chaos reigned. Mrs Frampton, craning to look at her husband, saw that he was not in his seat.

Oh damn. He's gone off in a huff. How am I going to get home?

At twelve midnight the Mayor stepped onto the stage and formal ceremonies began. First the major celebrities were introduced, thanked for supporting the charity, and made little speeches. Mrs Frampton, thrust this way and that at the back, could see little from behind the genial drunken crowd, but suddenly there was a gap, and she saw an empty seat and with a shove broke through and beat several others to it.

I wonder how long Little May intends to stay?

She looked round helplessly. There was no sign of her friend. Obviously, at this time of night neither of them would be able to sit out one film, let alone two.

At five o'clock in the morning, her face, like those around her, bathed in tears, Mrs Frampton stumbled to her feet and applauded and shouted '*Bravo*' and '*Olé*' over and over again. How could it be possible that Danny Auteuil, the handsome young Frenchman in the tuxedo who had given the amusing speech, could be the ugly, painful peasant Ugolin? His awakening sexual ecstasy on seeing the young girl dancing by the water without her clothes, the mixture of cupidity and pain, cunning and compassion that fought for dominance in his soul, and all shown on his face – Mrs Frampton had never seen anything like it. And Yves Montand! Of all actors her favourite . . . hearing the news that the hunchback he had hounded to his death was his own son . . . watching the depth of his grief . . . with nothing said . . . oh, that was unbearable. She knew, from having seen an interview he had done with Mavis Nicholson, that he had been suffering the grief of his own loss of Simone Signoret. And Mavis had asked if he had used his grief in the film and he had said yes, of course, because he was an actor, and that Simone would understand. Mrs Frampton had nearly not watched the programme, fearful of illusions of thirty years being destroyed. She'd loved old Yves ever since *The Wages of Fear*. Perhaps he'd turn out to be insubstantial after all. It wasn't unknown. But when Mavis had asked him about politics he had begun to shout passionately and wave his hands, saying that truth was more important than ideology, and things of such sense and conviction that Mrs Frampton, overcome with gratitude and love, had spilt a whole cup of tea in her lap. And Mavis, always the best of interviewers, not an interviewer really, more a woman who made you talk interestingly, had given him a look of honest liking and he had looked at her with a sort of deference, as to a woman, and as a colleague. It had been subtle, and adult, the mutual respect.

Thus Mrs Frampton, standing on the steps of the cinema as people swirled past her, smiled, full of thoughts and feelings. It would be no trouble to walk home. She'd never find Little May, but what did it matter? Passion and love gave you all the energy in the world.

She moved forward, shoved slightly by Princess Stephanie of Monaco and, looking ahead as she reached the bottom of the steps, saw her husband pull up in the Rover and get out and open the back door; and the Frenchies, seeming to erupt from nowhere, all climb in, bunching up their dresses and ducking to protect their hairdos.

'Hey! Vic!' shouted Mrs Frampton. She began to run through the thinning crowds, waving her arms. But the Rover swooped away and out of the wide white open gates.

Would you believe it! He had been there all the time! Vic? Sitting through not one but *two* films? It was inconceivable. Either that or he had gone home and come back to collect her – but no. Once home he would have been out like a light in five minutes. Surely the films hadn't pierced his armour, struck some distant chord of feeling. No. It wasn't possible. He had probably fallen asleep and been woken by the crowds surging past him. And wouldn't you know, he'd got collared by the French for a free lift home.

Never mind. The early morning air was like Beaume de Venise. With the scent of jasmine in the air Mrs Frampton, a hand on her bell-shaped skirt against the dust, set off down the road to San Pedro. Within a few moments a small green Renault drew up beside her. It was her neighbour from the pueblo, Señor García. He opened the car door and she got in. 'Ooh, am I glad to see you!' Her low sandals, fine for sitting, were already cutting in.

'Such films,' he said softly.

They drove in silence, slowed by other homegoers and early morning lorries, until, as they reached the avocado groves he murmured, 'There is a fine fisherman's café here on the beach. You would wish breakfast?'

Mrs Frampton, who had been too nervous to eat supper, was suddenly ravenous. 'Luis, that's the best idea since the sewing machine.'

He smiled, showing a gold tooth like a gypsy, and swung off the road and down the sandy track to the sea.

Chapter 15

THERE WAS SOMETHING the matter. Mrs Frampton couldn't put her finger on it. A year or so ago she would have diagnosed her sinking feelings as a leftover of homesickness, a recurrence of moods of insecurity in a new country. Or she would have put it down to the hot weather. Not the food, since she did the shopping and prepared most of the meals. In perpetual summer you didn't eat a lot, and the local fruit and vegetables were delicious, tasting as she remembered things tasting in her childhood. The fish? But it was so fresh the poor things turned desperate eyes on you on the weighing scales, and even HE had been demanding less meat during the endless summer days.

No, it wasn't the food and it wasn't the weather. She felt well in herself and HE was in a positively balmy mood. The sound of his whistling came piercingly from the bathroom every morning, he carried her baskets from the supermarket without a murmur and even, on one memorable night, had agreed to join in the quiz competition at the club. (That had been a mistake. He had come last and been sullen for days.)

After all those years of begging for a foreign holiday! And all it had taken was one go of pneumonia.

It frightened the life out of him!

Mrs Frampton, stirring her coffee out on the patio, looked up with pleasure at the vine leaves trembling in the light breeze. It was true, there *had* been moments when she had doubted the wisdom of their flight to the sun. She sucked in her teeth remembering those awful early months, knowing no Spanish, fearing to lose out to a bankrupt property company, a fraudulent builder. You read such horror stories, of buyers left stranded without a roof over their heads, of elderly residents milked to their last peseta.

And then we found it. El Pueblo La Jolla.

She smiled to herself, indulging in a favourite memory.

That moment . . . when we drove off the main road and down the lane past the farm, and then seeing the white gates and the view of the sea . . . I thought I was coming into paradise . . . Two pools and the gardens, and there's the beach, and our own café . . . There was even, now, a tiny shop where you could get bread and milk and yesterday's English papers.

Who would have thought, a few years back, that I'd have spent the morning talking politics under a palm tree with a Swiss and a Finn and two Frenchies!

It was true. You talked to people here in a way you never would at home. People felt let off the leash and the Spanish themselves were so open. There were at least eight houses and apartments in the pueblo where she could walk in with a 'cooee'. Gudrun and Mrs Miller were pals. Above all, there was Little May, the sly, shy, delightful Little May with whom she had become so close. We're sisters, thought Mrs Frampton, smiling to herself with pleasure. And dropped her scissors. That was it! That was what was unsettling her. Of course! It was Little May.

There was nothing you could put your finger on. Only the week before they had been to Málaga to choose some mousseline-de-soie for a charity dinner. Little May had been quiet, but this was not unusual, and when for no reason Mrs Frampton had turned to her suddenly and said, 'What's the matter, May?' she had looked at Mrs Frampton for the briefest moment and then smiled and said that nothing was the matter. Probably down half a million or something, thought Mrs Frampton, picking up her scissors and taking out the tacking of a skirt. Little May had recently returned yet again from Hong Kong. All that way! And, not for the first time, Mrs Frampton thanked her lucky stars that she wasn't cursed with an over-abundance of wealth and its seeming responsibilities.

At least HE was on the up and up. She hardly ever saw him. He must be making friends, she thought, and thanked her stars again for the fourteen golf courses on the Costa and all the sailing clubs and marinas with their convivial clubhouses. There was no doubt about it, the coast was designed for people to enjoy themselves. And why not?

I must write to Chloe!

On a whim, she jumped up and fetched her writing case.
Chloe had just been out to see them with her new husband
Patrick. The swift meeting and decision to wed had been a
surprise but, to Mrs Frampton's relief, Patrick seemed a
thoughtful man, not the roaring Irish boyo she had feared.

'Oh Mum, you old racist!'

She was in love all right.

Thank the Lord, thought Mrs Frampton. To have that, even
if not for ever. It's awful never to have that just once in your
life.

It was a recurrent source of sadness to Mrs Frampton. She
had been in love as a girl, had misinterpreted a look and
believed her love returned, only to have her hopes crushed. She
had never known reciprocal desire. Her own marriage to a man
she did not love had come about through panic. In those days,
if you didn't get a ring on your finger, you were a flop.

She finished the letter to Chloe and added a postscript. 'Your
father's more chipper than ever, he's becoming a dandy . . .
striped shirts and aftershave!'

She thought I've been neglecting the old so-and-so lately. I'll
make him something nice for his lunch.

She went into the kitchen. What should it be, scrambled
eggs and smoked salmon? No. He didn't like fish and thought
eggs were for breakfast.

'We have to change with the times,' she had said.

'Why?'

I might as well stop looking, she thought, as she heard the
garden gate click.

'I was going to do something fancy but I expect you would
prefer sausages, wouldn't you?'

He came through to the kitchen, his shirt open at the neck,
carrying the English papers.

'Not necessarily.'

'Oh, you've changed your tune.'

'There's a lot I've changed.'

'Good. I'm glad to hear it. What do you fancy?'

'I don't know, what have you got?'

She opened the cookery book at random.

'*Riz de porc*? *Brandade de Morue*?' she asked brightly, expecting to get a thick ear.

'I wouldn't mind a blanket dee voh. Can you do that?'

She looked at him in surprise.

'Well, no, not in a hurry I can't. I could have a go tomorrow if you want.'

'Don't worry. You have to know how to do it.'

He went into the living-room, leaving her open-mouthed with annoyance. What was that supposed to mean? She beat up eggs for a mushroom omelette. He must have been down at the club getting fancy ideas.

It'll be those Frenchies showing off as usual. Likely.

Mrs Frampton had no opinion of the culinary abilities of the Frenchwomen. They talked a lot but dinner invitations were rare since all three were meaner than a rat's behind. When Mrs Frampton had eaten at the lanky Eliette's she had dined on a frail lettuce salad and a meagre wafer of unadorned fish.

She called out, 'Lunch in five minutes,' put on the potatoes to sautée and set the places under the vine.

She heard him grunt, and then, a moment later, utter loudly and triumphantly, 'Well, well. Well, well, well!'

He came out, taking off his glasses, and thrust the newspaper on the table in front of her.

'Something there that should interest you.'

There, on the front page, was a small picture of Little May. Beside a larger picture of her son John.

For a moment the garden swam round her. Mrs Frampton sat down. And picked up the article. Her hands began to shake. John Liu had been arrested. For alleged dealings in drugs . . . heroin . . . on a massive scale, millions of dollars. Mrs Frampton began to feel very faint. She sat with her head between her knees for a few minutes, then got up shakily, went into the house and turned off the water for the peas.

'You'll have to get your own lunch.'

He looked up from the other newspaper.

'I always knew there was something funny about that Chink of yours. What did she want with you, for a start? You're going to have to watch out.'

She looked at him for a moment and then fetched her hat and glasses.

'I'm taking the car.'

'I shall be needing it.'

'Too bad.' She moved quickly and took the keys from the mantelpiece. And went out.

At first she feared that Little May was not going to receive her. Announcing herself at the gate as usual, she was kept waiting for some minutes. But at last the gates opened and she drove in with her foot down and round to her favourite parking spot by the stables. She hurried to the side door and Nina, the old maid, let her in and pointed silently across the courtyard to the garden. Little May was sitting on a seat at some distance with her back to them, by the nearer, narrowed end of the lake. Mrs Frampton approached silently on the grass and called quietly, 'May?'

Little May turned and rose, and came towards her. She paused, several yards away, and said gently, 'He says it is not true. But I think it is true.'

They went into the house together.

Mrs Frampton stayed with her friend until midnight. When the gates opened to let her out she looked about her in amazement. There were cars everywhere, and cameramen. As she edged onto the road they came towards her shouting and letting off flash bulbs. She accelerated, her heart thumping as a man banged on the roof and another attempted to step out in front of her, and drove off wildly. At home she parked under the pines and hurried into the house and to the telephone. And rang Little May, speaking carefully, as they had surmised that the telephones from the Casa Morisca might be tapped. Satisfied that Little May was calm, and that she had taken a mild sleeping draught, Mrs Frampton walked into the sitting-room.

The light was off. He must be in bed.

He'll be fed up with me, walking out on his lunch.

She went into the bathroom and turned on the taps, padding about quietly so as not to wake him. Lying in the warmth, she thought of Little May. It was a mess, no doubt about it. And Little May herself was in a strange mood.

I know what it is. She's wondering how much of what she owns, of what she spends, comes from drugs.

The thought was awful and she got out of the bath and dried her hair with the towel. Why did this have to happen? Just when everything was going so smoothly, so elegantly. She put on her dressing-gown. There was no point in brooding. Everything had to be dealt with in turn, as it happened. She looked for her book and remembered that it was in the sitting-room. As she descended there was a ring at the bell, and then a loud knock.

'Oh my God!'

Her fears for Little May rose like something toxic in the air so that she gasped. But when she opened the door it was Eliette, the Frenchwoman, who stood there, and behind her Simonette of the rinse.

Mrs Frampton stood firmly in the doorway blocking their entrance. If they had come for news of the scandal (and at this time of night!), well, they could just go back to where they came from. But Eliette pushed past her, straight through the open hall into the sitting-room.

'Where are they?'

'Who?'

'Where have they gone, do you know?'

'No – who?'

'You mean you don't know?' and something in Henna Rinse's stare made Mrs Frampton turn very uneasy indeed. She looked from one woman to the other. And, in doing so, noticed the letter propped up against the figurine of the Norwegian girl on the mantelpiece. Moving very slowly, she crossed and took it down. On the envelope was her name – May.

In *HIS* handwriting.

The letter went on for five pages. It was incoherent but he had never been a letter-writer. The gist of it was complaint, of neglect, of not being master in his own house, of money being spent, ha, that was a laugh – none of it made much sense . . . had he been drinking when he wrote it? On the last page he wrote, 'So I'm making other arrangements. If you're not prepared to cook for me there are those who will.'

She turned to the other two women who stood motionless and uncharacteristically silent.

'He says he's gone away.'

'Yes!' screamed Henna Rinse.

'With Henriette!' yelled Beanpole.

What?

'What?!!' Mrs Frampton gazed at them both, at their hostile, affronted, alarmed faces. And burst out laughing.

Chapter 16

Mrs Frampton's life seemed to be flowing past her like the Rhône in full flood.

Who would have thought it? After thirty years of marriage to the most miserable old cheese-parer in the world I end up on the Costa del Sol the friend of a Chinese millionairess with a tycoon son on an international drugs charge – and my husband's done a bunk with a Frenchwoman!

And not just any Frenchwoman, she thought grimly, but one of the thorns in her flesh from the day she had taken a seat by the pueblo pool and been patronised by the lanky Eliette, Simonette of the unsatisfactory divorce settlement and Henriette, who was known to have said once to the runner-up in a local track event, 'You should have run faster, then you might have won.'

What could you say about the woman without laughing? In the first place she was nothing to look at, a bandy camel came to mind . . .

Now May, there's no need to go getting spiteful. Still. After all, if you were going to be replaced you presumed it would be by a superior model.

If that's his choice, where does it put me?

These were dangerous waters. Mrs Frampton decided to lay off. After all, there was no harm to the woman. She did no work but, on the other hand, she caused no trouble, apart from the laugh. From somewhere she had an income. There had been no mention of a Monsieur, although she wore a sapphire and diamond eternity ring. Pointless to ask, of course, since the woman never made any sense. Both her Spanish and her English were non-existent and after five years she had still mastered neither the national currency nor the pronunciation of Madrid.

Let's face it, she isn't a hundred pence in the pound.

How on earth had the two of them got started? What language did they use? And what did they talk about? It was all so baffling that the imagination soon went on hold. Mrs Frampton, worried about Little May and the catastrophe that had befallen her, found that she could only dwell on her husband's defection at odd moments. There were more tragic matters at stake. Little May herself was calm, even authoritative. She stayed in the house, beleaguered by pressmen, telephoning, writing, sending telexes, talking to advisers. Mrs Frampton and the lawyers, thanks to the kindness of Sheikha Fahri who owned the adjacent estate, were able to enter the house via the Sheikha's garden. The Sheikha herself sent her daughters daily with flowers. Meanwhile, Little May's ordeal continued, fueled by the media.

'Don't read it – don't listen!' begged Mrs Frampton, and Little May nodded agreement. But a secretary took notes, tapes and videos for her perusal. There was little that Mrs Frampton could do – in fact, she suspected May of finding errands for her, particularly after the revelation of her husband's flight. Little May, on being shown his letter, had looked at it gravely, handed it back in silence. And then her mouth had twitched. And, despite everything, they had both rolled about on the pale sofas, giggling helplessly.

'He's awful, isn't he?' gasped Mrs Frampton, who had long ago confided everything to her friend.

'You are released,' said Little May, wiping away a tear.

A week passed and there was no word from the runaways. Mrs Frampton every day expected the axe to fall, for her credit to be withdrawn from the bank – indeed, prudently, she had gone the very next day and drawn out five hundred pounds in pesetas and laid in plenty of food and cleaning stuffs using her credit cards. Oddly, the thought of impending penury did not worry her.

I ought to be making plans, seeing a lawyer.

Her common sense told her that he would try to do her out of every penny. The house was in his name, to have suggested anything different would have caused wrath of sensational proportions.

I really should do something.

But a peaceful and dreamy languor set in. The house was quiet. Luisa, the pueblo maid, arrived as usual and, as usual, did very little except sing.

The gardener came in to gossip and drink Coke . . . she never left enough for him although their maintenance contract gave them his services. She spent whole days at the Casa Morisca, even secreting May out for a drive in the hills. But May had been anxious away from the telephone and after half an hour they had turned seawards again.

On the Friday evening Mrs Frampton, back from an afternoon's hair appointment, found a note from the office under her door. A Doctor Sanchez, from Ronda, had telephoned. Her husband, Victor Arthur Frampton, had been taken ill.

She left at once, packing an overnight bag and a spare pair of his pyjamas. She stopped once and telephoned to leave a message for Little May, and then drove on swiftly, familiar with the road, her mind clear and focused. The silly fool. Trust him to get himself into a mess. This wasn't his sort of thing, it was bound to all go wrong. What could be the matter? His chest was clear, he'd been well enough at his last checkup, overweight, but heart and lungs sound. A breakdown? It seemed unlikely, the last thing in the world.

Emilio, the pueblo porter, had given her precise instructions. Soon after crossing the glorious bridge into Ronda she drew up at the clinic. Inside she gave her name and was asked to wait. After a few moments a grave young doctor emerged in a brown suit.

'Señora Frampton?'

'Yes.'

'I am sorry. So sorry.'

He waved her down and sat beside her, taking her hand.

'Do you mean . . . are you saying my husband's dead?'

He nodded, looking at her gently with his soft, dark eyes.

'I see.'

But she didn't see at all. His voice came at her strangely, as if through a funnel.

'Do you wish to see him now?'

She nodded and he rose, and helped her to her feet. They walked along a pale pink corridor. At the end of it, on a yellow seat, sat Daftie, looking like a forgotten heap of laundry. She seemed unaware of Mrs Frampton, who followed the doctor into a little room. Where Victor lay, all his high colour gone, his face unlike him with the bones already beginning to show. The doctor disappeared and Mrs Frampton sat down. And began to cry for her husband, lying so composed, and so horribly still.

'Oh Vic – what have they done to you?'

She sat for over an hour. She sat, looking at him, holding his hand and thinking how miserable his life had been. Blaming herself for marrying when she hadn't loved, for not making him happy, for not making him better than himself, for loving Michael and Chloe more than him – for excluding him, and for despising him. Now it was too late. The wrongs had been done, and could not be undone. She had known more. So more was expected from her.

'I failed you, Vic.'

The room was so still. And yet it seemed as if she were not alone. And she had a sudden memory of a day she'd forgotten years ago, when he'd had a motor bike and they'd gone out and spent a day by the river. He'd been happy that day. Something had happened at work to please him, they'd had a picnic and lain in each other's arms, watching the swans and the moorhens.

'That was a nice day. We did have a few good times. And you did well for yourself. You got there. You made a bob or two.'

The light began to go quickly as it did here in the south. The room seemed cold. Bitterness began to invade.

No, none of that.

She rose and looked down at him. Who would have believed it? Who could have thought that amazingly, at the very last minute, he'd found what he'd always lacked, a brief moment of imagination. He'd made a bolt for it, for freedom, for something other.

'Good on you, Vic. If that's what you wanted . . . '

The room darkened and Mrs Frampton rose, hollow-legged,

feeling strange and weightless. She bent and kissed him on the lips, and laid her hand against his cheek for a long moment. But he was gone from her. She looked down for the last time at the beaky profile and then walked swiftly out of the room.

Outside, on the yellow chair, Henriette was still sitting. This time she saw Mrs Frampton and looked up at her with a terrified gaze. Mrs Frampton took her by the elbow, and she rose at once without resistance.

'Come on, my dear. Let's get you something to drink.'

Chapter 17

THE SIX MONTHS since the death of her husband had passed almost without Mrs Frampton's being conscious of it. She was brought up short by the date on her *Daily Mail* as she drank her mid-morning Nescafé one morning under the olive tree. The time had passed so swiftly.

I'd no idea it was so long since I lost him!

Lost in more ways than one. She smiled ruefully to herself, making the basket chair creak as she put the cup down. It was still something to be put away, to be thought about later, the remembrance that her husband had taken off in the company of Madame Henriette Isabelle Marie-Giselle Le Maistre, to die of a massive heart attack in a small hotel in Ronda, the ancient town where the fighting bulls came from. In one sense Little May's predicament had been a personal godsend. Her daughter Cinthia, married to an American Congressman, spoke to her mother daily on the telephone, but it was decided, to avoid publicity, that she should not join Little May. Mrs Frampton had been called into the breach. The proceedings still dragged on miserably, but at least the crowd of pressmen had given up and left the gates of the Casa Morisca. Mrs Frampton was now able to visit without creeping through the gardens of the Sheikha Fahri, who, with her passionate daughters, continued in staunch support.

When she was not at Little May's, there was plenty for Mrs Frampton to do. Michael had come from Australia for the funeral of his father with his new wife Steffi, a shrewd, lanky girl with an infectious sense of humour and a look of the film actress Lauren Hutton. And Chloe had come with Patrick. She had been seven months pregnant, looking so beautiful, her skin so glorious, that people in the street turned for another glance. The funeral, in the bright sunshine, had been poignant and slightly unreal. Afterwards the terms of Victor Arthur's will had been revealed and were, at least in part, as expected. Nothing to his son, whom he had treated with inchoate resentment from birth, thirty thousand pounds to his daughter Chloe and the remainder, something over one million, eight hundred thousand pounds, to his widow, plus the house at the Pueblo La Jolla, some parcels of land at Estepona, and a newly acquired small farmhouse in the hills behind Benahavis with sixty acres of land.

Which had all been extremely surprising. Mrs Frampton had not known he was worth half so much. So this is what he had been up to at the bar of the golf club every lunch time. He had been doing deals with the rest of the old boys. And what of the beautifully restored little house in the hills, with its pale, newly washed walls and lemon and orange groves, and the lady's silk scarf left on one of the window sills? Had this been intended for his new life with Daftie? In the circumstances, it seemed heartless to enquire.

But the money! Mrs Frampton, in a rush of extravagance, ordered a splendid lunch at Romano's new restaurant. The tables were set in the sumptuous gardens overlooking the dark blue sea and she asked for caviare and champagne, for special flower arrangements and for a decorative iced pudding of splendid proportions. After the champagne, Steffi, her new daughter-in-law, sang 'My Way' with one of the waiters, and an elderly German baroness broke into 'Lili Marlene' and capered on the terrace showing the tops of her stockings. Mrs Frampton, drunk, insisted on writing out a cheque for thirty thousand and thrust it into her son's pocket. But he jumped into the fountain and the water ruined the writing. It was a lovely, a joyous, a suitable day. The right send-off for Vic. For Vic, who had escaped into romance with his Frenchie (even if she did look like a tapir.)

Let's hope he had a few days enjoyment.

Probably more than that. Remembering his whistling in the bathroom, the aftershave, the new stripy shirts, she smiled to herself. He must have been courting Daftie for quite a while. He had been enjoying a secret assignment. Unbelievably, at the end of his life, he had had a bit of fun.

*

Against the joys and expectations of her newly enriched state,
however, were the shadows surrounding Little May – who remained on the surface serene and alert, even good-humoured –
but who worried Mrs Frampton who sensed something strange
and terrifying behind the gentle smile. She had nursed
depressed patients and was acquainted with the dazzling
brightness of desperation, with misleading and unnatural calm.
Little May, barricaded with money and servants, alien of
background, had never been easy to read. It was tempting to
dismiss fears, to thrust away suspicion. But Mrs Frampton
remained vigilant.

The day of the opening of proceedings in Hong Kong against
John Liu drew close. Little May, competent and calm, packed
yet again for the journey. Mrs Frampton took instructions on
various charity matters, in particular on the house for the
handicapped of which they were both active trustees.

'Don't worry, May, it will all be seen to.'

'And Benefacio's teeth?'

'I've already made the appointment.'

'I am not sure, you see, how long I shall be in Hong Kong.'

'You'll stay as long as you're needed.'

'Yes.'

And the friends had fallen silent. Since the moment outside
on the grass, when Little May had blurted out, in a manner so
unlike herself, that she believed her son to be guilty, though he
swore his innocence to her, this subject had not been raised
between them. It lay like a slab of stone on the heart. The
morning came for Little May's departure in the private jet.
Mrs Frampton accompanied her to the airport and was left on
the tarmac with tears in her eyes, clutching a small posy of
orchids, her friend's last thought.

She was at tea in the café of the pueblo reading aloud a letter to
Gudrun when one of her neighbours brought over the English
papers from the shop. She put them aside and went on with the
letter. 'William, I'm afraid, is a little devil, into everything.
Your godchild, May Rose, is the sensible one, never makes a
fuss and already loves to draw and make marks on paper, she's
only happy with a pencil in her hand. Lucinda's quite

different, she's a squawker, but a great sense of rhythm – she never sits still!'

'Well,' said her friend Gudrun, 'you are congratulated there, I think.'

The miracle had happened. Flora Kershaw, after Mrs Frampton's insistence, had received treatment at the in-vitro clinic from Michael himself, had been successfully reimplanted with three embryos and carried all three almost to term. She had sent a photo of herself, amazingly large and looking dazed. And then a sheaf of pictures of the three, with herself and her husband, both looking even more dazed. But happy. The husband, Tim, had been in remission from his leukaemia for over a year and was even working part-time. Mrs Frampton, who was a healer, chalked this up as one of her own successes though, she conceded, at arm's length. There had been earlier small events in hospitals when she had 'called' patients back, gazing up at the ceiling and instructing them to return when she thought they'd given up too easily. There had been one dramatic occasion when the surgeon on his rounds had bent over a motor-cycle accident, pronounced him dead and added that it was as well, since the boy, had he lived, would have been a vegetable. And Mrs Frampton, Sister Griffiths as she then was, had looked up and muttered, 'Come on down, Ian, come back at once and get walking.' And he had. Of course, you couldn't prove anything.

After pouring another cup of tea for them both and signalling to the waiter for further hot water, she glanced at her *Guardian*, scanning it idly. And news of the triplets paled. On page two, in a small paragraph, she read that proceedings against John Liu had been dropped for lack of evidence. She picked up the *Daily Mail*. Here there was a larger piece with a picture of Little May's son emerging from the court. She leaned back, breathless, and handed the paper to Gudrun.

'Well, so it is over.'

'I hope so.'

'He is innocent, is he not?'

'It says they haven't enough evidence to charge him.'

'You mean that his character is not cleaned up?'

'No, I don't think he's cleared his character.'

'Then this is not so good.'

Mrs Frampton, thinking of Little May, was silent. Gudrun drank her tea and ate two biscuits.

'He is not in prison, so we are happy, yah?'

And she smiled her dear, country smile which never failed to cheer Mrs Frampton.

'Yes, we're happy.'

Chapter 18

DURING THE ABSENCE of Little May in Hong Kong Mrs Frampton began to enjoy an expanding social life. At first she made a point of going out, both to relieve her anxieties on her friend's behalf and to assuage the loneliness of her early widowhood. The house was silent, spectral and accusing. It was better to accept any and every invitation, and when none was forthcoming to go out anyway, to be on the street with other people, even if only to eavesdrop, to watch children play or to window shop. Twice a week she went to the local cinema, and tried to make out the rapid Spanish dialogue. That still left the nights to get through, and here darkness regularly invaded. She read more than ever and bought another, smaller television to go in her bedroom, hiring videos of old thrillers and, best of all for getting to sleep, mindless American musicals of the fifties. From time to time she thanked her stars that she was not in one of the grander villas with gardens that had so tempted her when they had first been escorted round the area by the local agents.

Thank God he was too mean to let me have my own way, she thought. How on earth could she have survived, sitting on her own on some silent slope waiting for burglars to arrive. Here in the pueblo she felt protected. Emilio brought her fresh eggs from his daughter's farm, Mrs Coombs and Mrs Miller asked her round to play cards, and there were the societies, Literary, Musical and Garden. The nuns at the Casa del Lago too, seeming to understand her need, made more requests than usual. She drove about fulfilling their errands, enjoying the drive up the secret valley, the view of the house with the lake beyond, the warmth of greeting. Each time she came away burdened with gifts: fruit and flowers and honey, an embroidered handkerchief, a wobbly pot; once, a small carved saint painted in cheerful reds and blues. She shared the fruit and honey among her neighbours and the pueblo staff and felt comfortable with the old country style. It was good living, it was civilised, unpretentious and festive; though along the Cadiz road, building proceeded remorselessly. An old farm became a new hotel, a beloved nursery was suddenly closed and blocks of flats rose to cover the fertile soil. Soon, in the not too distant future, the country ways would go; already the shops were larger and noisier, gift emporia taking over from the haberdasher's, the cobbler's, the traditional pharmacy with the old man in the white coat.

But, with the news of John Liu's release, Mrs Frampton felt a lightening of spirits. Another year had begun. The tiny yellow daffodils on the slopes behind the pueblo had been replaced by ribbons of tall, white narcissi along the verges and under the locust trees. There was a feeling of resurgence, of life renewed, pristine and splendid. And the feeling burst into glorious joy with the excited call from her son-in-law Patrick in the middle of one February night.

'May, is that you?'

'Patrick? – Hullo, how are you, how's – '

'Well, hello there, Gran!'

'No!'

'Seven and a half pounds, long dark hair – '

'What is it, a – '

'Born without the least murmur of trouble, we were only in the hospital for two and a half hours before – '

'Patrick, what – '

'Chloe's sitting up eating Cream Crackers and cheese from the woman in the next bed's cupboard – '

'Patrick – '

'The baby's tucked under her arm like a little doll . . . '

'So it's a – '

'What?'

'Patrick! Is-it-a-boy-or-a-girl?!'

'A girl . . . it's a girl! The most divine creature you'd ever see in this world!'

'Oh! That's wonderful. I suppose it's too early to ask what you're calling her?'

'Not at all, her name is Adela Maeve Christina, hope you like it.'

'Oh Patrick' – Christina was Mrs Frampton's second name.

In the morning her neighbour, the widowed Señor García, came in for coffee and they celebrated with a bottle of champagne. Mrs Frampton became rather silly and laughed a good deal and pushed the little Luis off his seat and ruffled his hair. He, for his part, became dolorous, fixing his sombre eyes on her with a yearning, and even holding her to his sparrow bosom for a moment as she shed a tear of joy. When she flew to London to see her granddaughter he insisted on driving her to the airport and, on her return, laden with Polaroids of the baby, Luis García, was there to meet her. And they dined together and drank champagne once more. And Mrs Frampton, what with the flight and the champagne, felt ill all the next day, so ill that the ring of the garden gate went through her head like a hot wire and the bunch of lilies from Señor García seemed more appropriate for her wake than a thank you for a festive night out.

After her son's release Little May had flown from Hong Kong to America to be with her daughter Cinthia and to see her grandchildren. Mrs Frampton wrote, and sent a picture of Adela Maeve Christina, and received a little necklace of real pearls as a present for the infant.

I shall give a party, thought Mrs Frampton. I can do as I want, now. I'm going to invite the whole pueblo to wet the baby's head.

This posed problems. After the death of her husband in Ronda, Henriette, with whom he had decamped, had been deposited by Mrs Frampton back in her apartment. This, fortunately, was at the other end of the pueblo, close to her two friends, the bossy Eliette, and Simonette, the whining sidekick of the Day-Glo hair. However, a party in the pueblo would mean their presence – not to invite them would create an impossible awkwardness in the small community. Mrs Frampton had hoped that Daftie, as she had always privately called Henriette, would have had the decency to move out of the pueblo. But on reflection she realised that the woman was so dependent that this would have implied the exodus of all three musketeers, and the other two were unlikely to make the sacrifice. So, from time to time, May Frampton would catch Daftie's eye by the pool or in the bar. And the little woman would colour up and look away. At least it meant that the Frenchies stayed clear. What's more, there had been one or two re-sales in the pueblo and Mrs Frampton's own 'set' had been augmented by the MacGregors, a jolly pair of tipplers, sharp as scissors, and by a young couple, Viv and Terence and their two boys, Jake and Marty, who livened up the pueblo no end. And what with the Beanpole working overtime enlarging her boutique, and Simonette, the other one, doing a full-time receptionist's job, a new daily pattern had settled amiably in the pueblo. There *was* unfinished business. The necessity to give Madame Henriette Le Maistre a crisp right to the jaw was an obligation that at some time must be fulfilled.

Whichever way you look at it, Vic was a fit man when he left me. Five days of Daftie and he's lying on a slab.

What on earth had the pair of them got up to? It made your mind spin even visualising them in the same room. Mrs Frampton, getting into her lonely bed at nights, found her thoughts turning to Luis García. He was a nice man. She liked him. They shared a love of plants, and of people, of things that grew. They liked the same books. Twice now she had been to his modest apartment over the pueblo café, once to watch his video of Cocteau's *Beauty and the Beast*, which she had found too French and overdressed for her taste, and once to try his paella, which had been good but heavy.

I could drift into something there.

Why not? She missed the presence of another body in the bedroom, another presence in the house. Despite his snoring, his sour body smells, his hawking and spitting, his habit of picking at the scurf on his scalp, the way he ate, the way his behind stuck out when he walked . . . everything really, she missed Vic. It was salutary to admit to herself that despite the fact that she had despised his meanness, his tunnel vision, his smug subjectivity for thirty years, she was now lonely without him.

People aren't meant to be on their own. It isn't natural.

And it made her smile that, despite all the bridge-cracking smiles of the Frenchies and others of her acquaintance in the pueblo, all younger and thinner, she might be the one to acquire a genuine suitor. She renewed her membership of the beauty clinic and now, unabashed in her black bathing costume, swam in the larger pool every morning before breakfast, careless of being seen, and once catching Señor García at his window watching her.

What a turn up that would be. It gave you something to do, looking after a man.

I've looked after people all my life. I must do something, find somebody.

In the end the celebration for her grandchild became a trip to Córdoba. She hired a minibus and went with the MacGregors, deaf Mrs Miller, Mrs Coombs, Gudrun and the young family, the Ingrams. And Luis García and his nephew Freddi. The day was balmy, the children shouted under a small waterfall discovered on the way. Córdoba, with its fine buildings and famous courtyards decorated with flowers, was explored and marvelled at, and wine was drunk.

'I think,' said Gudrun, the next day, 'when we are going to do this again?' And Mrs Frampton was pleased. But the real joy was to follow. Chloe and Patrick and baby Adela were to come for two weeks, for a holiday. Soon.

And Little May returned. Mrs Frampton, waiting in the separate lounge, missed her friend emerging from the aircraft. When she did look up, she saw a tiny, old, yellow-faced woman with huge burning eyes. And her soul turned over.

The friends embraced and were soon together in the back of the dark blue Rolls. Mrs Frampton found herself talking rapidly, gossiping, telling stories, filling in details of the well-being of the nuns and their charges in the house in the hills supported by Little May, reporting, as she had been doing by letter, on the progress of this child's speech therapy, of that patient's improved behaviour, and of the success of the new plantings in the gardens of Little May's home, the Casa Morisca. Earlier, they had pored together over David Austin and Peter Beale's catalogues. Mrs Frampton had introduced her friend to the work of the two breeders who had bred roses back to old varieties to regain scent, sublety and gentler colouring.

'Wait until you see them, May!'

'I shall look forward to it,' the little woman had replied, her face creased and yellow against the blue leather of the upholstery. There was no life in her. No life at all. Mrs Frampton spoke of her new grandchild, and took the latest photograph out of her handbag. And Little May looked. And smiled. And held the picture in her gloved hand for a moment. What's the matter with her? What have they been giving her, thought Mrs Frampton, who had no illusions about the mischief of doctors who attended rich women. They drove in silence for a while. It was no good. She turned to her friend and said, 'May, you look awful.'

Little May looked at her and smiled a faint smile. And nodded infinitesimally.

'Are you on anything?' She was about to say drugs but thought better of it. 'Are your doctors prescribing tranquillisers?'

'Yes,' came the soft, slow reply.

'They're not doing you any good.'

'Oh,' the soft voice came with a sigh. 'I don't take it.' And she looked Mrs Frampton in the face. 'There is nothing to be done.'

'Of course there is!'

Honoré, the chauffeur, took the next long bend with perfect precision.

'Listen.' Mrs Frampton took her friend's tiny hand.

'You've been through more than any mother should have to. But your son is free and you are home – you say this is your home, that your heart is here, well, you're back and I'm going to make you well again. I'm not having you looking like this!'

'Too late.' The sound came so softly that Mrs Frampton thought she might have misheard.

'Sorry?'

But Little May did not reply at once. The car bowled through the pine groves of Calahonda and the two women sat in silence, Mrs Frampton with her new short hairdo for the occasion, Madame Liu tiny, her face strangely creased and lined, in the corner. Then, as they approached the sumptuous golf courses of Los Monteros she said, suddenly and clearly, 'He is guilty.' And her face was like a wooden carving, grained, fixed and implacable. And there was nothing more to be said. At the Casa Morisca they drank tea, and Mrs Frampton spoke of her daughter's arrival, two days hence. Little May smiled and said how happy she must be and Mrs Frampton agreed and, soon after, went away.

'Don't get up,' she said, and Little May, who always accompanied her to her car, smiled and stayed where she was. At the door of the salon, looking in a mirror, Mrs Frampton saw the small reflected figure, a tiny, rigid icon by the vast Spanish fireplace. She groaned aloud as she made her way to Honoré and the waiting Rolls. On the way home she leaned forward.

'Look after her, Honoré.'

'*Oui*, Madame Frampton, *oui, oui*.'

'She isn't well.'

'That shows itself.'

'Then it's our job to make her better.'

Honoré, in the seat in front of her, shrugged his shoulders in an elegant, inimitable French gesture. He was right. It wasn't going to be easy.

Chapter 19

MRS FRAMPTON LOOKED in at her guest bedroom with satisfaction. The white marble floor was good enough for a palace. They had paid extra for it at her insistence, the house having been unfinished when they bought it. She smiled, remembering his yells of complaint.

I was right. It looks like a fairy tale.

She surveyed the white bed, the white quilted cloth over the dressing table . . . she had seen that idea in a *Country Life* . . . and the large green monstera in the blue and white pot, the only splashes of colour in the cool, white room.

Just wait till Chloe sees this!

She had redone the room as a celebration of her new grandchild. How good that she had insisted on a three-bedroomed house! Adela would sleep in the new cot in her own little room through the archway, with the new blue cotton curtains with the appliquéd rabbits. These had been made by Mira, the large Dutchwoman, who was always running out of things to sew.

I can't believe they're coming.

And to cap it all there had been a letter from Michael and Steffi to say that he was taking a post in Baltimore. They would be oceans closer, a mere flight away within a couple of months.

Mrs Frampton's smile faded as she went downstairs. There was only the one fly in the ointment. In that beautiful house up the road from King Fahd's palace Little May sat silent and alone. From the day that her son had successfully evaded charges of massive drug smuggling his mother had become a recluse. The Costa del Sol, sanctuary for criminals, chancers, false titles and ne'er do wells, would have welcomed her back with open arms. Engraved invitations, particularly to charity functions (for Madame Liu was known to be a generous patron), showered through the letterbox by the gate of the Casa Morisca. But May Liu sat in her salon, her hands folded in her lap. She continued to receive Mrs Frampton, who talked of this and that, and who kept a close eye on her for vital signs.

There was little to perceive. Little May continued to look dried out and wooden faced, yellower than ever, her eyes sunken and dark. Mrs Frampton feared a tumour. It couldn't go on. She spoke to Alvarez, one of Little May's doctors. Who said that yes, the patient was evidently not herself. That she was not co-operative, was not responding to treatment, and that he had advised travel.

Useless, thought Mrs Frampton to his fat backside, you're just covering yourself, mate.

But then her beloveds arrived, safe and sound and, thanks to her friend's generosity, she was able to greet them with Honoré and the open-topped Mercedes. Adela, with four teeth, and distinctly red hair, leapt into her arms joyously, just in the way that Chloe had always done, like a young frog. And for the next ten days Mrs Frampton never stopped singing. They visited Little May for tea, and Mrs Frampton was pleased to note that May for once had some colour in her cheeks, and that she gazed at the baby, and actually came out into the garden with them for a walk. She even responded to Patrick's easy Irishness, and talked Middle Eastern politics (his subject) for a while, with a sharp astuteness.

I must bring them again, throught Mrs Frampton.

But first there was the trip to Seville. Preparations were completed. They were to stay for the night in Seville itself and then on to Córdoba and back home via Granada. Mrs Frampton made notes, plotted the routes, and baby-sat in the evenings for the children to get out and enjoy themselves.

It was on the second such evening that Luis García called on the telephone to ask her to an evening of Spanish song and dance.

'I'd like to, Luis, but I can't. I'm baby-sitting.'

'A pity.'

'Never mind. It's the Pavarotti *Bohème* on Gib. TV.'

'Ah! I didn't know!'

'Do you want to come and watch it with me?' The reception on his own set was bafflingly varied.

'I should like that very much.'

'Oh but . . . don't you have tickets for the other thing?'

'I tear them up.'

'In that case, I'll give you supper.'

He arrived on the dot with a gift of quails' eggs. Mrs Frampton had prepared an easy supper which they could eat on their laps while watching Pavarotti. Between the acts she bobbed out for the melon and nectarine salad and the coffee while Señor García, who had provided the wine, recharged the glasses. At the end of the opera, after all the curtain calls, as they looked at each other, their heads full of music, glory and poignancy, Luis García, in the middle of opening another bottle, suddenly slid to his knees. And asked Mrs Frampton to become the second Señora García. In other words, to marry him.

'Oh Luis! Don't be such a ninny. You're drunk.'

'No. I am not. I am not drunk.'

'You'd better get up before you fall over.'

'Not until you answers me.'

She laughed and he jumped up and grabbed her masterfully and kissed her. He missed her mouth the first time, but not the second. Good heavens, so *that* was what kissing was like!

An hour later they struggled up from the sofa, dazed with wine and kisses and he bent over her hand.

'I ask to you.'

'You're going to feel an awful fool in the morning.'

'No. You are so fine.'

'Oh, get on.'

'I ask.'

'Well, I'm not answering. Ask me some other time, when you're sober.' And she had steered him out of the door, putting his jacket on his shoulders.

When the children returned she was standing in the debris of the meal with a silly smile on her face. They looked at each other and at the two plates and the two glasses, and smiled discreetly and whispered together in the shadowy white bedroom before falling into passion. And the baby woke and

143

sat up in the new cot and chattered quietly to herself for an hour, as was her habit, until, at the first light of dawn, she fell asleep, bum in air, as the sparrows began to chatter on the roof.

Saturday dawned clear and bright. They were to leave at nine, but it was well after ten by the time Mrs Frampton's new Volvo brake drew away with Patrick at the wheel. For two mornings there had been flowers from Luis and she sent him a Graham Greene paperback with a silly note. There would be time to get into all that later, when the children had gone. Time now for their trip, for a voyage through mythical Andalucía. They bowled along the road with the windows open, Adela crowing softly in the back to the purr of the car.

'That's the way to your friend's isn't it?' asked Chloe.

'Yes. I should have telephoned this morning. I'll ring from Seville.'

'That house is the loveliest I've ever seen.'

'I agree.'

'And you know why?' said Chloe, who was a graphic designer.

'Simplicity.'

'I know what you mean. I don't know how much is because she's Chinese and how much is because she's May,' said Mrs Frampton. She sighed. It seemed unfair to be happy when her friend was sitting in all that beauty in such despair. But today was not the day. No worries. Today was the day for a trip with her loved ones, under a clear blue sky, in the south of somewhere where she had always wanted to be. She was in the money, off the hook, and on the loose.

'Stop the car,' said Mrs Frampton. Patrick, obedient to the sharpness in her voice, pulled up at once.

'Turn back.'

'Why?' Chloe, in the back with the baby, leaned forward.

'We must go to May – quick, as fast as you can, Pat. I'll tell you where to turn off . . . there's a short-cut!'

Chapter 20

M RS FRAMPTON, ON many occasions, had had reason to be thankful for her nurse's training and experience. And less often, but occasionally, for a strange prescience which caused her to act out of character, as when she had rushed from the cinema in the middle of a film to find the kitchen curtains ablaze and the baby-sitter asleep. Or when, as a small child, she had screamed so hard for her father that they went to fetch him from the stable loft and found him with his pelvis broken. It was the same feeling . . . a deep screaming within, a coldness in the bowels that made Mrs Frampton shout to her son-in-law to turn the car from Seville and drive at once to the Casa Morisca. Patrick, the Irishman, had given her one look and obeyed without a word. As they arrived, the gates opened, which was unusual as the lodge screening normally took a moment or two. This time the woman leaned out, saw the blue Volvo, and within another minute they had sped up the main drive.

'Stop here!'

Mrs Frampton ran, panting, into the house.

'May . . . May!'

Luis appeared, followed by Nina, the elderly maid.

'Where is Madame?'

'She ees aslip, Señora Frampetan.'

Mrs Frampton took the stairs two at a time and tried the bedroom door. It was locked.

'Fetch a key.'

But there was already a key on the inside of the door. Mrs Frampton banged and called.

'May! May, it's me, May . . . May, it's May!'

She lifted a hand for silence. There was not a sound from within.

'Fetch a ladder.'

Outside, in the garden, they looked up at the window and Patrick said, 'I don't need a ladder,' and climbed up the magnolia grandiflora and over the sill in ten seconds. He called, 'I'll open the door.' And Mrs Frampton ran back into the house and across the courtyard and up the wide staircase followed by three maids, two gardeners and Honoré, with Chloe and the baby below, gazing up in bewilderment. And into the bedroom. Where Patrick already had Little May on her feet.

They were almost too late. May was in a deep coma. Patrick and Honoré walked her up and down as Mrs Frampton telephoned for an ambulance. Two hours later she was sitting in a private clinic waiting for news. The doctors emerged at last, harassed but now without panic.

'She will be well.'

'You used a pump?'

'Oh, yes.'

'Is she awake?'

'No.'

'I should like to sit by her.'

'Of course, *Señora*.'

'You go,' she said to the children, 'look, it's your holiday, the room in Seville is booked, just cancel mine.' But they kissed her and shook their heads, and she cuddled Adela for a moment and smelt the top of her head. And went into the bedroom.

Little May seemed to displace no volume at all. She lay, a barely discernible mound below the pale counterpane, her eyes closed, her face immobile, her breathing thankfully regular. Mrs Frampton took her hand and spoke gently.

'Look, May – I'm here. I want you to rest now. Have a good, deep sleep and come out of it ready to fight. No more of this sadness. It's no good, it doesn't get you anywhere.'

Little May made no sound or movement. Mrs Frampton settled down in a comfortable armchair and read a magazine, and then ate an omelette brought by a silent, smiling nurse. And then dozed. She woke, and Little May had moved slightly and was sleeping now on her side. She looked more natural and

Mrs Frampton rose and tucked in the sheet. And felt less tense. The doctor looked in the door.

'You can go. She will be fine.'

'No, I must stay.'

'Of course.'

Little May woke just after nine in the evening. Mrs Frampton was looking out of the window at the tops of the pines when she heard a faint sigh. And turned to find her friend's eyes fixed upon her.

'How is this?' asked the tiny woman in a low voice. Mrs Frampton sat beside her and took her hand.

'I couldn't let you do it.'

'I asked them not to disturb me.'

'Don't blame the staff. I made them open the door. Patrick got in the window.'

There was silence.

'I don't know,' said Little May at last.

'Well I do,' said Mrs Frampton. 'You're needed. Happy or sad, you have work to do. We need you,' and burst into tears.

'Oh, how unpleasant it must have been!' said Little May. And she sat up. Mrs Frampton sobbed, then sniffed, then blew her nose heavily. There was silence again.

'Tell me,' said Little May diffidently, 'was I sick?'

'No.'

'Had I – did I – '

'If you mean had you wet the bed – no. You looked very peaceful, Patrick said. I didn't see, he had you on your feet by the time I got in the room.'

'Without my dressing jacket?'

'I put it on at once,' lied Mrs Frampton. 'And Honoré carried you gently down the stairs.'

'In front of the servants?'

'No, no,' Mrs Frampton lied again. 'We went out by the side door.'

The two friends sat for a while and then Mrs Frampton got up and rang the bell, causing Little May to look up in alarm.

'I'm going to order some food for you.'

'Please, no. I cannot eat.'

'You're going to, though, because I'm going to feed you.'

She ordered some consommé and a little plain rice and lemon tea.

'I shan't eat it,' said Little May.

'We'll see.'

Mrs Frampton stayed at the clinic for three days. She accompanied her friend home and stayed overnight. When she returned to her own home Chloe cooked a fine meal of roast lamb and coffee pudding and they talked till the small hours. Patrick and Chloe and the baby were brown and relaxed, full of sun and fresh air. The next three days were blissful, lazy and mindless. Twice a day Mrs Frampton drove to see Little May, who reclined, docile and non-committal on a *chaise-longue* in the petit salon, a book on her lap. On their last day, at her friend's request, May Frampton brought her family to say goodbye. Little May gave Patrick a first edition of Yeats, Chloe a delicate muff chain of moonstones and Adela a Little German carousel which played a Schubert air. Mrs Frampton, watching for signs, began to hope for recovery. The presents had been exquisitely chosen. Her friend *must* be feeling better.

But when, after seeing off her family at Málaga airport, she returned with an armful of freesias and came upon her friend unobserved, she saw that she had been mistaken. That her hopes had been false. Little May had been misleading them. She was not well. She was not well at all. Mrs Frampton went home to an empty house with a leaden heart. She talked on the telephone to Honoré in his fine apartment over the stables of the Casa Morisca and he reassured her. A close watch was being kept on Madame, as the doctors had ordered.

As Mrs Frampton, unable to find the energy or will to cook dinner, was making her way to the kitchen with a bowl of cornflakes, the garden gate bell rang. It was Luis García.

'They are gone and you are lonely so I come.'

How good it was, just for a while, to give up, to hand over to someone else. She had spoken to him briefly after Little May's removal to the clinic and he had offered his services. Now she told him everything, with discretion on her friend's behalf, and he listened and nodded, all the while moving from her kitchen to the patio preparing a simple salad and laying the table for two.

'I feel chilly,' said Mrs Frampton. So he lit a fire in the sitting-room and they ate together with the food on their laps as they had on the night of the opera. After a large brandy he turned to her.

'Of course, you have not been able to think of my question to you?'

'Question?'

'What I have asked you.'

'Oh – that.'

It was true. The near tragedy at the Casa Morisca had driven the proposal from her Spanish widower neighbour from her mind. She sat, her thoughts muzzy with the brandy, his arm about her shoulders. Well, it would certainly be a lark, looked at one way. Almost worth it just to infuriate the Frenchies! They had never ceased to speculate on the putative possibilities of Luis García as a lover since he'd lost his wife from a fishbone in the throat three years back. And they made eyes at him. He might have one of the cheaper apartments in the pueblo, but he was one of three brothers who jointly owned extensive farming land on the other side of Jerez. His modest exterior concealed a distinguished background, with relations in government, a heroic uncle from the Civil War, now a legend, and an art expert cousin in Madrid.

Wouldn't I like to spit in their eyes! thought Mrs Frampton, sliding a glance at her suitor, glass in hand at her side. He wasn't a tall man, but he was muscular, younger than she, probably about fifty-five. His hair was going but it was still dark. Perhaps . . . and, oh yes, wouldn't it be nice to be able to sit back, let someone else do all the paperwork again! A little voice within said softly, Be careful, May, you did it for the wrong reason last time, but, before she had time to bring that thought forward for inspection, the telephone rang. It was Honoré. He had been playing cards in the big kitchen, and Nina had run in to say that Madame was weeping. Mrs Frampton returned to the sitting-room.

'Luis, I'm sorry. I've got to go over to May's – she's not herself.'

He got up.

'I unnerstan'. You wish me to drive you?'

'No . . . I'll probably stay the night, I'll need my car in the morning.'

'I shall come with you, and walk back.'

'Good! It'll clear your head!'

When she reached her friend it was to find her in the bathroom, sitting on the edge of the bath, wracked with sobs.

'Go on – cry, cry it out,' said Mrs Frampton gently.

'What is the use? I may cry until I die, and what is achieved?' She said, stumbling, that she must sell everything, her houses, her jewellery, everything, including her clothes. Despite the fact that her wealth came from the successes of her financier husband, she felt tainted. Since his death her son had handled her affairs. To her great advantage.

'We'll talk of it in the morning.'

'You want me to live?' Little May's face was almost unrecognisable – twisted and distraught, almost venomous, like the frightening faces of some mental home patients.

'Of course, you know I do . . . '

'Then I must make the terms.'

'You want to give it all away?'

'Yes.'

Eventually, Mrs Frampton persuaded her friend to bed and gave her her prescribed sleeping draught. She walked through the silent, beautiful rooms, pausing to look at the Marie Laurencin, mysterious in the half-light. In the courtyard moonlight created huge, leafy patterns.

What a shame.

But, in a way, the place was too beautiful. Too empty. A museum to loveliness. Better if it *were* to become a children's home, a maternity clinic, a school for the handicapped. Was it right for one human being to own so much in the face of want? If Little May chose to expiate the crimes of her son thus, why not? Perhaps if she did her vitality would return.

If necessary . . . if necessary, I've got enough dough for both of us, thought Mrs Frampton as she drove along the silent, moonlit lanes. What a strange reversal that would be. And she thought I can't marry Luis. Sheer indulgence, what on earth was I thinking about? Sheer greed. In any case, May needs me.

She let herself in the side gate and, followed by Mandarina, the kitten from next door, went up to bed.

Chapter 21

IT WAS NEARLY Christmas. The streets of Marbella and San Pedro were festooned with lights, and the shop windows, crammed with glacé fruit and mountains of plump local almonds and stacked with expensive imported tins, shone in the mild sunny weather. Mrs Frampton, released into the independence of widowhood, shopped with concentrated inventiveness and made pretty parcels for Mrs Miller, who was going home to Croydon by the Santander ferry, to post in England. Her presents for Steffi and Michael had been air-mailed in November.

'Come over for Christmas!' Steffi had begged over the telephone.

'I can't. I'm going to May's.'

'How is she?'

'About the same.'

'Can't you get her to somebody – a priest or a psychiatrist?'

'I've tried.'

They changed the subject to Steffi's early pregnancy for an expensive thirty-five minutes.

What Little May's formal religion was Mrs Frampton had never discovered. Certainly, she practised the Christian virtues of humility and charity. At the same time, her house was full of valuable furniture and priceless paintings and she spent heavily on clothes and jewellery. Until that anguished moment when she had cried out to Mrs Frampton that all must be sold. Mrs Frampton had pondered equably on the notion that their roles might be reversed, and that she might possibly be the provider for her friend in the future. But, since that agonised revelation, Little May had slipped into a passivity helped, Mrs Frampton suspected, by the over-generous medication prescribed by her private doctors. In the last three months her own visits had settled into a thrice-weekly routine. She had taken over some of Little May's charitable responsibilities. Every Sunday she paid a visit to the home in the hills and faithfully reported on the residents' progress on her return, filling out her account with as many lively anecdotes as she could muster.

It was with surprise, therefore, that Mrs Frampton, on her arrival at the Casa Morisca after an ebullient morning's shopping for more presents, was told that Madame was in the garden. For months now Little May had sat silently indoors with a book on her lap and Fortunato at her feet. Mrs Frampton's heart leapt at the news and, waving aside old Nina's offer to go and seek her employer, she made her way to the seat by the lake where Little May liked to sit. But there was no one there, nor along the formal cypress walk, nor in the rose gardens. Mrs Frampton began to perspire. She retraced her steps and circled the lake. There she paused and sat down for a rest, looking at her watch. Twenty minutes since she'd arrived. She stifled a sense of anxiety. No, it wasn't so. Little May was all right. But where was the silly woman?

Mrs Frampton got to her feet and plodded up the *alleé* of pleached fruit trees, across the fine green grass to the large, irregularly shaped swimming pool. The water lapped softly. No one. A bird skittered up, shrieking. She crossed and went up the flight of steps to the heated pool that gave into the house. And, as she reached the top step, saw a little girl in a blue patterned bathing costume and a pink floral cap sitting on the edge of the pool dangling her legs in the water. No, it couldn't be! It was Little May – who waved as Mrs Frampton approached, and waved again, smiling.

'You look wonderful!'

'The water is very pleasant. Not too warm.'

'Have you been swimming?'

'Look, try.' And Little May dipped her hand in the water and let the drops fall playfully.

Mrs Frampton kicked off her shoes, sat down and put her feet in the water. 'Ooh, that feels good. I've been shopping.'

'For Christmas?'

'Yes, for the family.'

'Did you buy something nice for me?'

Mrs Frampton, startled by the playful tone, said truthfully, 'Not yet. I haven't quite made up my mind.'

They sat together in silence and Mrs Frampton watched the birds on the other side of the pool hopping in and out of the palms, chattering and quarrelling. One of the maids in the house burst into song, hoarse and passionate. And then stopped. Little May said softly, 'I am happy.'

Mrs Frampton looked at her as she gazed out at the water. And marvelled. Her friend's profile was as smooth as a girl's. As it had been before. What had happened to the yellow old woman she had become in the last six months? Mrs Frampton, her thoughts utterly confused, looked away. And Little May said in a serene voice, 'John is dead.'

Mrs Frampton's head turned sharply.

'Your son?'

Little May looked at her, looked in her eyes, her face shining.

'Yes. He has killed himself.' There was silence for a moment. 'Each time he came to see me he said it was not true. He laughed and smiled and scolded me for my thoughts.' She paused. Mrs Frampton waited.

'He came on Sunday.'

'You never said.'

On Mrs Frampton's last visit May had been as usual, listless in the Louis Quinze chair.

'No.'

There was silence and then a burst of song from the kitchen, urgent and wailing. And once more, quiet. Broken by a tiny sigh.

'This time he did not laugh. This time he wept.'

'You mean . . . Are you saying that he . . . '

'Oh yes.' The sound was barely audible.

Mrs Frampton said carefully, 'Did you know that he was going to kill himself?'

'He asked my permission.'

'And you gave it?!' Mrs Frampton sprang to her feet and gazed down at her friend, her eyes wide and unnatural.

'May! He's your son!'

There was silence again except for the girl in the kitchen whose song now diminished to a tearing, sobbing growl like an animal spent at the end of a chase. Little May looked up and said, 'He was my son. My first-born.'

Mrs Frampton looked at her friend. She looked at the bright bathing costume, the festive cap of rubber petals in pink and blue and yellow, at the colours of celebration. And it felt just as though her own heart was bleeding inside her chest. She sat down heavily on the stone paving and took her friend's hand. But could not look at her. Little May said, 'I know that you find this very hard to understand. For me this is not the end of my son. It is his beginning. He has paid his debt, in part, at least. He could do no less. It was his wish.' And she jumped up and said, 'And so you see . . . I am happy! I have made him happy, so I am happy!'

Mrs Frampton gave her her wrap and they went into the house together. After tea Little May called for her photographs, and for the rest of the evening they pored over pictures of John, and of Cinthia, his sister, but mainly of John . . . John in his pram, with his first puppy, John at the helm of his sailing boat, playing tennis, diving; John in bed recovering from appendicitis, John with a leg in plaster at Gstaad.

'I think that he wanted to be more success than his father. His father was cold with him.'

'Yes,' said Mrs Frampton. 'My husband was always jealous of Michael. It was my fault. I didn't love my husband. I loved Michael and Chloe, but not him.'

'Perhaps my fault was greater,' said Little May in her tiny voice. 'I loved my husband first. Oh, I love my children, but I followed my husband everywhere, I could not bear to be without him. I only saw myself through his eyes. Without him, who was I? And then he died, and I had to find out, anyway.'

'But you loved your children?'

'Yes, but I didn't put them first.'

'And you think women should?'

'Oh yes. Of course.'

'I don't know,' said Mrs Frampton.

'They must know that you are there. I was not. It is unnatural.'

'So you blame yourself – for everything?'

'As you did when your husband went away.'

Mrs Frampton said, loud and firm, 'Then we're fools, both of us! And I wish you'd take off that silly frilly dress and get into some decent black and start mourning for John.'

Little May stared at her and looked away.

'Never mind whose fault it was. He chose to pay for what he did in this way. You're his mother. Your job is to grieve, to mourn his loss.'

But Little May hummed to herself. And Mrs Frampton left soon after and drove herself home in a dangerous mood.

Christmas in the pueblo was a jolly affair with prolonged eating and even more drinking. Little May left for America to be with her daughter and did not return for three months. The wild muscari and the white narcissi bloomed along the hedgerows, the sheets of blue iris followed and the first asphodels came into flower. Mrs Frampton went to Tangier and Fez with Gudrun and Eliette and the MacGregors. And Luis García called and was attentive and his friendship with Mrs Frampton grew closer and began to cause comment. They were easy together. She talked Spanish with him and he corrected her grammar, and she was teased by Gudrun who accused her of corralling the only available man in the pueblo. And all the time Mrs Frampton's thoughts returned to the absent Little May. There had been two short notes and a beautiful flowering bush in a square Chinese pot, delivered on Mrs Frampton's birthday. But no real news.

And then, on a very warm March day, as Mrs Frampton was hacking off the huge lower leaves of the palm by her orange trees, the telephone rang. It was Honoré, the chauffeur, the portly shrewd Honoré, who sometimes looked in for a cup of coffee and a gossip. He had rung to say that Madame was at home once more, that she sent her very best wishes to her friend Señora Frampton and hoped that she would call as soon as possible. The next day, fetched by Honoré in the blue Rolls, Mrs Frampton went to the Casa Morisca. And there was her friend – pale, smooth and shining in a black silk dress.

The two friends greeted each other gravely. They drank tea

together and ate petits fours, and exchanged news of grand-children. After the silver tea-tray had been removed there was a slight pause and then Little May said, 'I have been busy.' She waved a hand. There, on a side table, were the new plans for the Casa Morisca.

'These will be the classrooms, here the gymnasium, these the treatment rooms, here the extra cabins for sleeping.' Casa Morisca was to become an adjunct of the Casa del Lago in the hills, a school for the physically handicapped. 'To be named the John Liu School.'

'That's grand,' said Mrs Frampton.

'Of course, it will need many to run such an establishment. We shall need good staff.'

'Yes,' said Mrs Frampton.

'Come and sit down. Give me your advice.'

At seven another tray appeared with salmon sandwiches and almond biscuits and a large pot of coffee. At eight Mother Catalina and two nuns arrived, obviously by arrangement. At eight-thirty the young architect called, and added his voice. Just before midnight Mrs Frampton shook her head at a request to stay the night and Honoré was summoned from his cards to drive her home. Mrs Frampton said, 'I've a lot to think about, May.'

Well, she thought in the garden the next day, here's a fix. I'm just nicely set up, my house as I want it with room for guests and grandchildren, a good dressmaker, decent dentist, good doctor who even looks like Ray Milland, and now . . . and then there's Luis. It's all very well, but what about Luis? She tied in the tendrils of the jasmine with bass, cutting out the flowered shoots, frowning in the sun without her hat. She paused and sighed, and sat back on her heels. It was so good to have a man about the place with his dark, shaven face and his smell. She was washing and ironing his shirts now, it had started as a favour after a glass of wine had been spilt, then it had become a joke, her superb laundering. Now it was a fixture.

I like looking after him. I'm used to it. Helping Mum and Dad with the boys, then Vic and the children. And he likes it. He doesn't need it, he's well organised, but he likes the affection.

Couldn't there be a bit of affection still?

Yes. Of course. But not marriage. That was over. It had been a long haul, but the children were reared, both his and hers. Companionship, yes, affection, yes, from time to time. But there was only one thing left that was really worth doing. Little May might have her reasons, but it was true, anyway. You had to work. If you didn't work you were old. You were past it. But while you could see and hear and get about, and understand what was said to you, you weren't old. You couldn't use it as an excuse.

No. It was no good. Luis would find somebody else in the end. If he did, good luck to him. Mrs Frampton struggled clumsily to her feet and went inside and through to the telephone. And dialled. When Little May came on the line she said, 'May. The answer's yes. I'll take over as general supervisor. I'll move in at once; I haven't made up my mind yet what to do about my house, but I may sell it and put the money towards the physiotherapy department. We must be properly equipped, that could be down to me.'

'Good,' said Little May. 'I am busy now. Would you like me to send Honoré to collect you?'

'No, I'll drive myself. 'Bye for now.'

'Goodbye, May. Oh, and May?'

'Yes, May?'

'Oh . . . nothing.'

From the other end of the telephone came a little giggle. Mrs Frampton put down the telephone and leaned against the banisters. And smiled ruefully to herself.

Who would have thought it?